CHARACTER STEINS

CHARACTER STEINS
A Collector's Guide

EUGENE V. MANUSOV
MIKE WALD

Illustrations by Claire Hill

CORNWALL BOOKS
NEW YORK • TORONTO • LONDON

Cornwall Books
440 Forsgate Drive
Cranbury, NJ 08512

Cornwall Books
25 Sicilian Avenue
London WC1A 2QH, England

Cornwall Books
2133 Royal Windsor Drive
Unit 1
Mississauga, Ontario
Canada L5J 1K5

The paper used in this publication meets the requirements of the
American National Standard for Permanence of Paper for Printed Library Materials Z39.48-1984.

Library of Congress Cataloging in Publication Data

Manusov, Eugene V., 1929–
    Character steins.

    Includes index.
    1. Character steins—Germany—Catalogs.
I. Wald, Mike.   II. Title.
NK4695.C52M34   1986   738.2'4   84-45009
ISBN 0-8453-4784-5

Printed in the United States of America

This book is dedicated to the three most important women in my life—my lovely wife, Pat and my two daughters, Vicki and Valerie.

—Gene Manusov

This book is dedicated to my favorite character, my daughter Ronni.

—Mike Wald

CONTENTS

PREFACE

IN 1976 THE *ENCYCLOPEDIA OF CHARACTER STEINS* WAS PUBLISHED. IT CONTAINED ALL THE knowledge that we had accumulated up to 1975 when the final manuscript was delivered to the publisher. As you read through the pages of this text, you will notice that we refer quite often to the descriptions in *ECS*. The *Encyclopedia of Character Steins* was published by the Wallace-Homestead Book Company (Box 81, Des Moines, Iowa 50304). Yet even as that book was being prepared for printing, Gene Manusov and I began working on this second volume; we know there was still much to be discovered. And, in fact, tremendous progress has been made since the first book, partly because that book increased the general awareness and appreciation of character steins throughout the world. Old and new character stein collectors brought forth a number of previously unknown steins and spent some time seeking out new information about character steins. The pictures in this book show these new steins; this section recounts some of the new knowledge.

Collectors like Werner Sahm, Roland Henschen and Lotti Lopez, through diligent searching, have been able to obtain copies of many original stein manufacturers' catalogs, some pages of which show original sketches or photos of character steins. Thanks to these researchers we are able to display in the "old catalogs" portion of this book some of these exciting finds from manufacturers such as Rosskopf & Gerz, Steinzeugwerke, Reinhold Hanke, Merkelbach & Wick, Marzi & Remy, and J. W. Remy. These catalogs have made it easy to identify the previously unknown makers of many character steins. They also show a great number of character steins that have not yet surfaced, a clear measure of the size of the task that still lies ahead.

In addition to these catalogs much new information has come from researchers who have recently published their results in *Prosit*, the quarterly publication of Stein Collectors International. One of these articles, by Lotti Lopez, in the June 1977 *Prosit*, concerns the substantial number of steins attributed in *ECS* to Steinzeugwerke, Höhr-Grenzhausen, Ltd. Lotti writes: "This company resulted from a consolidation of several 'no brand,' small factories and workshops, as well as well-known producers such as R. Hanke, Simon Peter Gerz and Reinhold Merkelbach. Because more than one firm was involved in the manufacture of different steins, including character steins, none were marked with a maker's name (exceptions exist). The Steinzeugwerke group was in business for only 13 years, from 1912–1925." So in this book we must again refer to many steins as "made by Steinzeugwerke" because we still cannot attribute pieces to individual manufacturers; however, we do now know the approximate date of their production.

Several marks that were not previously known have recently been identified with specific firms. For example, in the September 1979 *Prosit* Kurt Sommerich writes that the "F&M/N" mark belongs to Felsenstein & Mainzer of Nuremberg. According to Kurt, this firm turned out fine pewter articles including the all-pewter character stein of the Nuremberg Tower, *ECS*-418. They did not, however, produce the ceramic towers that bear their mark, but instead had them custom-made by another unknown factory. Nevertheless, it is quite possible that Felsenstein & Mainzer did make the beautiful pewterwork for those steins.

The "T.W." trademark is another mark that has been identified with a company, as reported by Steve Smith and Chuck McKittrick in the December 1981 *Prosit*. A porcelain stein in the shape of a kiosk had been discovered and on the kiosk were eight multicolored advertisements for Nuremberg firms (see Figures 1–4). One panel in particular was of interest for it clearly advertised a character stein of a blue/grey stoneware Nuremberg Tower with the "T.W." mark impressed into its base. The kiosk ad stated "Nurnberger Thurm-Seidel ½, 1/1, 2½ Ltr T W Gesetzl. Geschützt Verkauflich in den besseren Glashand-lungen," the last line of which translates into "purchasable in the better glass shops." The bottom of this important stein has a round mark with a T and W intertwined and the wording "Theodor Wieseler Glasmanufact. Nurnbg." If Theodor Wieseler was solely a *glass manufac-turer* and did not make stoneware or porcelain steins, then, as with F&M/N, he was having them made by another company and was distributing them. We are also familiar with this mark on *ECS*-239, 419, 457, and 466, plus MT-7, TO-8, TO-9, and TO-10.

Figure 1. Front view of kiosk stein depicting eight advertising panels.

Figure 2. Side view of kiosk stein showing one of the eight panels advertising a T.W. stein.

Figure 3. Close-up of advertisement of T. Nuremberg Tower character stein on kiosk.

It is also believed that the many steins marked "Martin Pauson, München" were contracted out to various stein makers and then distributed and sold under the Pauson name. There is, in fact, no evidence at this time that Pauson was a stein maker, decorator, or even a pewterer, although a number of pewter lids and straps have been stamped with this name.

Two other names identified with the Munich area are Josef Mayer and Josef Reinemann. For years collectors have been referring to these names as the manufacturers of steins. However, even with the extensive lists now available, no one has been able to find any ceramic or pewter workshops associated with either of these names. So here, too, there is the distinct possibility that these are names of distributors, and the names of the firms of the actual craftsmen who made these beautiful character steins has become a new mystery.

In fact, the practice of having steins made expressly for a distributor is still common today. We find factories such as Rastal-Werk distributing character steins made by the M. Girmscheid factory. We also know that Rastal purchases many stein blanks from the Gerz factory and applies their own decorations. We must assume that the same kinds of practices were probably common sixty to eighty years ago, which terribly complicates the task of identifying manufacturers.

A final area of newfound knowledge concerns the many different *tic-tac-toe* or *crosshatch* marks found on porcelain character steins. Many collectors are under the false impression that all crosshatch-marked character steins are from the so-called "Musterschutz" factory, the most prestigious maker of character steins. We all agree that *Musterschutz* simply means "copyrighted" but it is used as if it were a factory name because it is the only word on these beautiful steins. In the chapter of this book by Ron Fox he explains how to identify Musterschutz steins regardless of the marks on them. The crosshatch marks found with the word Musterschutz are in a light to medium blue color. A non-Musterschutz crosshatch is generally found in black and dark blue and is squarer rather than elongated. The non-Musterschutz crosshatch mark has been seen on some of the Gentleman Rabbits (*ECS-63* and 64), Bismarcks (*ECS-134*) and the Heidelberg Student (*ECS-190*, right figure). The Musterschutz steins were made around the turn of the century and were made in the Thuringia area. The non-Musterschutz steins are of a later vintage, some feel possibly even post–World War II.

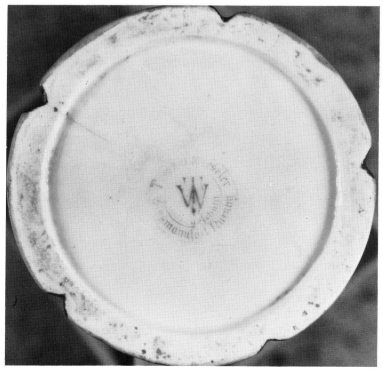

Figure 4. Base of kiosk showing T.W. mark along with the name of Theodor Wieseler.

Even with strong leads pointing toward a manufacturer, confirmation can still be elusive. Take, for example, the common inscription on character steins that reads "D.R.G.M. 154927." In August 1973, Steve Smith reported in *Prosit* that his investigations showed this mark had been issued on 9 April 1901 to Adolph Diesinger, "located in Höhr by Koblenz for the following: Machining to the exact and sharp demarcation of colors on porcelain, ceramic and majolica, etc., consisting of a hand-worked relief of all figures and decorative representation." Since 1973, even with all the hard work of collectors in Germany and especially in Hoehr-Grenzhausen, we have not been able to determine who Adolph Diesinger was—a stein maker, a stein factory owner, or simply a patent holder.

It must now be obvious that while there has been much progress in determining manufacturers there is still a very long way to go. Answers that are discovered seem to always raise new questions; new character steins that are "found" occasionally fill in known gaps but more often seem to carry unknown marks or styles. The hope of all who have contributed to this book is that the reader will become intrigued enough and curious enough to join us in the search for the answers to the questions that remain.

MIKE WALD

ACKNOWLEDGMENTS

THROUGHOUT THE LONG PREPARATION OF THIS BOOK THE AUTHORS HAVE DRAWN HEAVILY on the knowledge, experience, suggestions, and encouragement of a great number of individuals. Without assistance of this kind such a book could not have been written. The photographs, descriptions, and historical information imparted in this text would not be possible without the many "collaborators" who unselfishly shared their wisdom with us. We list many of these persons and express our deep gratitude for the unstinting cooperation offered.

Heading our list are three special contributors of excellent chapters. They have all been honored by Stein Collectors International with the prestigious award of *Master-steinologist:* Jack G. Lowenstein, Ron Fox, and the late Dr. J. Joseph Hersh.

A very special "danke" to our talented illustrator and former Miss Beer Stein of Stein Collectors International, Claire Hill.

We both acknowledge the important contributions by Gary Kirsner who made available any character stein he came across for us to photograph; many of them rare and unique pieces.

A tip of our chapeau to our "poet laureate," Art Maethner. His "free translations" may make some of our German readers wince—they may not be exactly accurate—but they are beautiful. We also thank him for sharing his vast knowledge of German history and folklore with our readers.

Special kudos to Werner and Rosemary Sahm of Hoehr-Grenzhausen who were very kind in allowing us to print many of their old, original catalogs. Many previously unidentified character steins were identified, thanks to these catalogs.

We extend special credit to our "Master stein collector," Bill Schwartz, plus our fellow collectors Roland Henschen, Lotti Lopez, Leonce Miller, and Dr. James Gruhl.

We also acknowledge (in alphabetical order):

Mel Alpren	Jill Bauman	Warren Brown	John Crowley
Bob Alutin	Lawrence Beckendorff	William Burkle	Don Daugherty
Hans Ammelounx	H. S. Black	John Caponi	John DeLuisi
Doug Armstrong	Urban W. Boresch	Phil Caponi	Jim DeMars
Neil Barton	Sam Brainard	Earl Christy	Roy DeSelms

Floyd Dietlein
Joe Durban
Mark Durban
Mary Durban
Alfonso Edmonds
Richard Ehlert
Bruce Ehly
Ed Ehring
Steve Elliot
Muriel Enslein
Fiore Esposito
Col. John Ey
Jack Feigenbaum
Don Forster
Don Franz
Bob Gray
Matt Gruskin
John Hamilton
Jim Hansen
Ron Heiligenstein
Harold Hemphill

Joseph Hermida
Terry Hill
Al Hoch
Spencer House
E. C. Innis
Aram K. Jerrehian, Jr.
Irv Johnsen
Stan Jordon
Dr. Glen Joshpe
Ed Kilduff
Herb Klein
Martin Levitt
Victor Lopez
Frank Love
E. G. Mattmiller
Eric Mayer
Dr. Norman Medow
Don McKim
Chuck McKittrick, Jr.
Henry O. Naetzker
Mario Pancino

Robert Papenfuss
Les Paul
Steve Pezalla
Frank Pociadlo
Frank Poppie
Bob Potash
Walt Rippert
Fred Roschow
Heinz Roes
Jon Rosenbaum
Tom Sage
Jim Sauer
Leonard Schenk
Jay Schlossberg
Prof. & Mrs. Adi Schmoll
Fredlein Schroeder
Louis Schultz
Ben Sherman
Kenneth Sherman
Dick Shetrone
Frank Sklar

Eugene J. Smith
Steve Smith
Jim Stevenson
John Stuart
John Tombro
Marvin Tschida
Cyril Volk
Bob Weinman
Bob White
Bob Wilson
Les Whitham
Ken Zeiser
Bob Zoebelein
Joe Zyla

Also: *Prosit,* the quarterly bulletin of Stein Collectors International; Berte and Graham Dry for permission to use their catalog page from Rosskopf & Gerz; *The Shekel,* vols. 13 and 14; Belgian National Tourist Office; and many others.

In addition to the many individuals above, a very special "kiss" to our lovely and patient wives, Pat and Shirley. We thank you both for encouraging us to "hang in" for those many years. We love you both.

GENE AND MIKE

INTRODUCTION: "OF BEER AND STEINS"

GENE MANUSOV

SHAKESPEARE DRANK IT. SO DID MARTIN LUTHER, MARY QUEEN OF SCOTS, AND ANNE BO-leyn. It is said that Julius Caesar gave a beer party after he crossed the Rubicon. Sir Walter Raleigh had some with his pipe the morning of his execution. Francis Scott Key drank it in Baltimore while he finished "The Star-Spangled Banner" (taking the tune from an old drinking song). Some say Thomas Jefferson polished off a couple at a Philadelphia tavern while he polished off his first "draft" of the Declaration of Independence. Before he discovered Libya, Billy Carter got his own press by talking about beer seven days a week. He's even had a brand named after him. Many members of Stein Collectors International are known to fill their favorite stein and quaff a liter or two.

Average consumption in the United States is about a six-pack a week for every adult—nowhere near the top of the world list, which is usually dominated by the, who else, Germans.

The Germans call it "bier," the Japanese, "biru," in Mexico it's "cerveza," and in the United States it's known as beer. In 1980 Americans consumed over four BILLION gallons of the frothy brew in cans and bottles marked with nearly six hundred different domestic labels. In addition to the domestic beers, Americans also managed to down several million gallons of foreign imports.

Beer goes back so far no one knows where it started. There was beer before there was real writing and maybe even before bread. Ancient Babylonians, Assyrians, Sumerians, Egyptians, Hebrews, Africans, Chinese, Indians, Incas, and others all knew of beer. In fact, of all the human cultures known, only Eskimos and certain desert tribes of southern Africa missed out—Eskimos because they had no grain, the desert dwellers because they had no water to spare.

According to one old Assyrian clay tablet, beer was taken aboard Noah's Ark. Sumerian workmen building temples were given about a liter of beer a day. Egyptians who slaved to build the pyramids drank mild beer made from the red barley of the Nile. They called it "hek" (or "haq") which sounds like what people say when they've had more "hek" than they should. Sometimes, though, beer in Egypt was known as "boozah" or "bouzy," from which derives our "booze." One Egyptian king gave "boozah" to his subjects and then tried to convince them that the good feeling it produced actually came from *him*. An Egyptian papyrus of about 1400 B.C. warns against beer's effects: "Do not get drunk in the taverns in which they drink beer, for fear that people repeat words that may have gone out of your mouth without your being aware of having uttered them." Sound advice.

Women often did the brewing in those early days, but in Babylonia around 2100 B.C., Hammurabi fired them all and hired men instead, leaving women to run the taverns.

Greeks and Romans, being in grape territory, drank far more wine than beer. For a long time Romans thought beer was for barbarians, although Pliny at least was impressed when he heard about beer for the first time. "A method has actually been discovered," he wrote with joy, "for making even water intoxicating!"

From way back when people have credited beer with medicinal qualities. A thirty-five-hundred-year-old Egyptian medical text recommends beer in various mixtures as a cure for scorpion sting, as a laxative, and, taken with half an onion, as "a delightful remedy against death." Jews in Babylon supposedly took beer to ward off leprosy. The Anglo-Saxons took beer as medicine for lung disease, lunacy, pains in the knees, and hiccups. Germans centuries ago maintained that beer helped their rheumatism and stomach ills. They called it "the soother of life" and "the oiler of joints." They served it in hospitals, saying, "The brewery is the best drugstore." French doctors of the seventeenth century prescribed beer for everything from smallpox to cancer. In this country in 1789 the Massachusetts legislature passed an act encouraging the manufacture of beer because "wholesome qualities of malt liquors greatly recommend them as an important means of preserving the health of the citizens."

Peter Stuyvesant erected the first American brewery in 1623 in New Amsterdam. A century later a number of Revolutionary War heroes were involved in the industry. "Father of the Revolution" Samuel Adams, Thomas Chittenden, the first governor of Vermont, and George Washington were brewers, and both Patrick Henry and James Madison were known to down their share.

"Beer" comes either from the Latin *bibere*, "to drink" (as in imbibe) or from Saxon *baere*, meaning "barley"; it depends on who you believe. "Beer and skittles" is English slang for fun and games (skittles, like "keggling" being a bowling-like sport). A "beer-jerker" serves beer. "Beer heart" is a problem of the ticker, supposedly caused by too much fluid consumption. "Beer belly" often follows.

By definition, beer is a fermented beverage brewed from malt (usually barley), yeast, and water, and flavored with a variety of hops. The resulting brews can be as fragile and complex as fine wines. Like wine, beer comes in a variety of flavors and strengths.

The most popular type currently consumed in America is "lager," and 90 percent of domestic and imported beers are in this category. Lager is effervescent, light amber, and has a mild hops aroma and flavor. The name comes from the German word *lagern*, meaning "to store" and refers to a cold-temperature fermentation process discovered centuries ago by monks. "Malt liquor" is essentially lager, but with a higher alcohol content.

"Ales," on the other hand, are fermented at slightly higher temperatures. While yeast falls to the bottom of the brew in lager processing, the yeast rises in ale, producing a lighter "hoppier" flavor and a stronger alcoholic content than lagers achieve. The British are fond of ales, and of their cousins "porter" and "stout" (ales with roasted barley, malt, or sugar added).

"Bock beer," brewed for nearly six centuries in Germany, is heavier, darker, and rather more sweet and hoppy than any other beer. This Bavarian specialty derives its mahogany hue from highly colored malts.

In recent years the ideal container for drinking varies with the packaging of the beer. Draught beer is best downed (if a stein is not convenient) from a large frosty mug (which keeps carbonate gas from escaping), but canned or bottled beer should be served in small glasses so the brew won't warm too quickly.

But it was not always so. Drinking vessels for beer, wine, and other liquid elixirs of the day have been found—often in the shape of an animal, figural, or head—dating to ancient times. The steins depicted in this book (from the middle nineteenth century to the present) are relatively new compared to the many character drinking vessels found in ancient days. The recent exhibition from the People's Republic of China, "The Great Bronze Age of China," showed several interesting pieces from the Shang dynasty (thirteenth–eleventh century B.C.)

Figure 5. Wine Vessel (guang). Bronze; 14¼″ (36.2 cm). Shang dynasty, 13th–11th century B.C.
(Courtesy of The Cultural Relics Bureau, Beijing and The Metropolitan Museum of Art, New York)

Figure 6. Elephant-shaped Wine Vessel (zun). Bronze; 9″ (22.9 cm). Shang dynasty, 13th–11th century B.C.
(Courtesy of The Cultural Relics Bureau, Beijing and The Metropolitan Museum of Art, New York)

Figure 7. Rhinoceros Container (zun). Bronze. Warring States period, 475–221 B.C.
(Courtesy of The Cultural Relics Bureau, Beijing and The Metropolitan Museum of Art, New York)

Figure 8. Drinking Vessel. Gold. 5th century B.C.

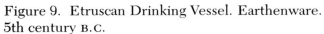

Figure 9. Etruscan Drinking Vessel. Earthenware. 5th century B.C.

Figure 10. Fox's Head. Stirrup cup. Silver-rimmed, black stoneware (basalt). Ca. early 19th century. Cups were handed to hunters for a final beer before the chase.
(Courtesy of the Fowler Museum, Los Angeles, California)

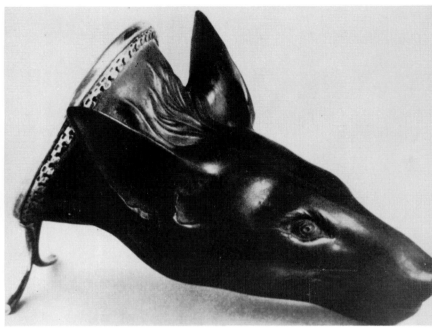

Figure 11. Drinking Cup. Silver. In the form of a rearing horse, possibly once completed with a rider. Liegnitz, early 18th century.
(Courtesy of the Fowler Museum, Los Angeles, California)

Figure 12. Drinking Cup. Silver. In the form of a rampant lion. Hamburg, last quarter of the 17th century.
(Courtesy of the Fowler Museum, Los Angeles, California)

Figure 13. Drinking Cup. Silver-mounted leather of a shoemakers' guild, the mount engraved with a man armed with a spear about to attack a lion. German. Mid-16th century.
(Courtesy of the Fowler Museum, Los Angeles, California)

Figure 14. Monkey Ewer. A Dutch delft drinking vessel. The animal is seated on a yellow mound base decorated with a red and blue trellis. A tricorn hat is painted in red and manganese.
(Courtesy of Sotheby's Auction house, London)

(Figures 5, 6). Another excellent example is found in the "zun" (Figure 7), a storage vessel in the shape of a rhinoceros, (from the Warring States period, 475–221 B.C.) whose massive body, with its heavy folds of hide at the neck, is decorated with intricate cloud scrolls that were once inlaid with gold. Egyptian drinking vessels are found in many Cairo museums (Figures 8, 9).

In recent centuries we have found drinking vessels depicting foxes' heads (Figure 10), horses (Figure 11), lions (Figure 12), drinking cups (Figure 13), and many others (Figure 14).

Beer has been with us almost forever, and so have the beautiful containers to hold it. Every time you pour a little of the lager into your character steins, think of the ancient heritage behind the beverage and the stein.

UPDATE ON *ENCYCLOPEDIA OF CHARACTER STEINS*

MIKE WALD AND ARTHUR J. MAETHNER

(Throughout this chapter asterisks indicate
steins made by Schierholz and Sohn.)

IN THE *ENCYLCOPEDIA OF CHARACTER STEINS* WE FEATURED 467 ILLUSTRATIONS SHOWING 469 steins. Since 1975, when that information was forwarded to the printer, we have learned much about these unique figural pieces. As we examined these pieces we found that some contained erroneous information, and in other cases, further clarification was necessary. We have discovered the identity of many of these steins and found other sizes, colorings, and variations.

We, with the help of many other collectors, have gone over each stein, figure by figure, and have updated what we have learned about them. Many of the variations and copies are illustrated in this edition.

ECS
Figure Number

1	**BERLIN BEAR**—This was a special edition for the Berlin Industrial Exhibition, 1896. It was originally made with a plain shield, minus this inscription. (See "Animals" AN-1, 2.)*
2	**SITTING BEAR**—The correct translation should be "Tenth German Federal Shoot, Berlin 1890." It has nothing to do with a republic.
3–4	**BOARS**—Both of these steins were made of porcelain. They are shown together in this book under "Animals" (AN-6).*
5	**CAT WITH HANGOVER**—Another version of this stein was made with the cat sitting on a keg-like base, which was made to support a music box (AN-9). It was also made in color (see "Animals" AN-8) and as a tobacco jar (see "Stein-related Items" SR-7, 8). The words *Sauren Harung* actually mean "Sour Herring."*
8	**CAT WITH FISH**—Art suggests a better translation should read "Full today, null tomorrow." This stein was originally made by Rosskopf & Gerz and can be found in their 1914 catalog also using Mold No. 420. (See "Old Catalogs.")

9	**CAT ON BOOK**—One of these steins has been noted with the Ernst Bohne [2c] mark.
11	**CAT**—Also made in ¼- and ¹⁄₁₆-liter sizes. (See "Animals" AN-16.) Most times this stein is found without the whiskers. The ¹⁄₁₆ liter version was also made with the cap on either the right or left side of the cat's head. (See "Animals" AN-17.)
13	**SITTING CAT**—Identified as J. W. Remy. (See "Old Catalogs.")
15	**CAT**—Made by Steinzeugwerke. (See "Old Catalogs.")
16	**CAT**—This stein was also made with a deep hollow base fitted for a music box. Another version of this stein shows the cat with a mandolin instead of a seltzer bottle. (See "Animals" AN-12.)
18	**SITTING DOG**—There were two versions of this stein made. The older one was well detailed, colored in a light brown, and carried a mold number on its base. The newer version, which is probably shown in *ECS*, carries no mold number and is colored a very dark brown. (See "Contemporary Steins" CO-33.) They were both probably made by M. Girmscheid.
19	**SHAGGY DOG**—This stein was also made in a blue/grey stoneware minus any base markings. (See "Animals" AN-23.)
20	**GENTLEMAN DOG**—The facial colorings vary greatly from stein to stein.*
21	**GENTLEMAN DOG**—This stein was identified as J. W. Remy. (See "Old Catalogs.") *Lumpenhund* is the German word for scoundrel or ragamuffin, but not scoundrel tramp dog.
22	**BULLDOG**—This stein is shown in an ⅛-liter size. It also was made in a ½ and ¼ size, sometimes in a dark brown color. (See "Animals" AN-25.)
23	**PUG DOG**—This Mettlach stein was made of stoneware, not porcelain. There were three main character steins made by V & B but other semi-character steins are featured in *ECS* and in this book.
24	**ELEPHANT**—Probably made by Steinzeugwerke.
28	**GENTLEMAN FOX**—This stein was also made in blue/grey stoneware. One version was seen in full color. (See "Animals" AN-31.) The figure shown, a *Fuchs* or "Fox," was the name given to first-year fraternity students at the university. Note the little "cap" and tri-colored ribbon over the right shoulder which marked and/or identified them as members of a fraternity or *Korporation*.
30	**HERR FOX**—This was made only in porcelain, never in pottery. This figure also refers to the first-year fraternity student, as does *ECS*-28. The stein base is the same as *ECS*-189.
31	**FOX**—This stein was also made in a ¼-liter size, probably as a set. (See "Animals" AN-30.)
33	**SAD MONKEY**—This is definitely not a monkey, but a chimpanzee.
35	**MONKEY**—This stein was probably made by Ernst Bohne.
36	**INEBRIATED MONKEY**—Probably made by Reinhold Merkelbach. The phrase "monkey on your back" is an American slang expression used to describe someone addicted to drugs. When the Germans say, *Er hat einen kleinen Affen*, "He has a small monkey," they mean that he is a little tipsy.
38	**INTOXICATED MONKEY**—Made by Steinzeugwerke. (See "Old

Catalogs.") Also made in overall cream coloring. The Hofbrauhaus may be Munich's most famous beer hall, but it is not the largest. That honor goes to the Buergerbraeukeller.

39   **DRUNKEN MONKEY**—This stein has been copied since World War II by R.P.M. in the 1950s and, more recently, by Rastal. (See "Contemporary Steins" CO-38, 73.) The Musterschutz version was also made as a tobacco jar. (See "Stein-related Items" SR-5, 6.)*

41   **MONKEY**—This Mettlach stein was made of stoneware, not porcelain. As in *ECS*-36, the phrase "Monkey on your back" is incorrect.

42   **SITTING MONKEY**—Made by Steinzeugwerke. (See "Old Catalogs.") The German phrase was written by Kaspar Koegler, a famous painter of the late nineteenth century, and a colleague of Heinrich Schlitt in Wiesbaden. "The beauty of the butterfly cannot disguise the ugly worm. The fleeting joy of the night before cannot excuse the morning after. So those who persist, and to spirits hold firm, are bound to encounter disaster." In other words, the ugliness of the caterpillar (hangover) evolves from the beautiful state of inebriation (butterfly).

43   **SITTING MONKEY**—Made by Steinzeugwerke. (See "Old Catalogs.")

47   **BARREL STEIN WITH MONKEY ON LID**—The base on this stein was used very often on Musterschutz steins. The same base or body can be seen on *ECS*-396, 397, 398, and 449.*

48   **MILITARY MONKEY**—Identified as J. W. Remy. (See "Old Catalogs.") This stein was reproduced in January 1980 by M. Girmscheid, minus the pewter lid rim using mold #837. (See "Contemporary Steins" CO-28.) For a better translation, see *ECS*-42 correction.

JUST BEFORE *ECS*-49 WHERE "PIGS" BEGIN—The pig or swine was often used on steins because it was seen as a symbol of good luck in Germany. The Germans traditionally ate far more pork than any other kind of meat. Hence, those who were able to enjoy pork were the lucky ones, particularly when times were bad.

49   **SITTING PIG**—Also made as a tobacco jar. (See "Stein-related Items" SR-10.)*

51   **PIG IN A POKE**—This stein is made of porcelain, probably by H. Hutchenreuter of Probstzella (Thuringia).

52   **BARTENDER PIG**—This is a post–World War II stein. Two newer versions of this stein were also made, one in earthenware by Hachiya Bros. in Japan and another by Simon Peter Gerz made in stoneware. (See "Contemporary Steins" CO-24, 54.)

53   **SITTING PIG**—Made by Steinzeugwerke. (See "Old Catalogs.")

55   **SINGING PIG**—Also made as a tobacco jar. (See "Stein-related Items" SR-9.)

56   **SINGING PIG**—Another version of this stein was made with the pig sitting on a keg-like base, which was made to support a music box, similar to *ECS*-57. (See "Animals" AN-44.)*

59   **PIG**—Identified as J. W. Remy. (See "Old Catalogs.") Should be *Deutsche Mark*, not *Deutsches Marks*, referring to the bag of money.

60   **PIG WITH CARDS**—Definitely made by Reinhold Merkelbach.

(See "Old Catalogs.") Another version depicts a shooter's motif in the pig's stomach panel.

61 **PIG WITH BOWLER**—Also made by Reinhold Merkelbach, mold no. 1116. Note the difference in the ears of *ECS*-60 & 61.

62 **GENTLEMAN RABBIT**—This famous Musterschutz stein varied greatly in facial colors from stein to stein (see Figure 27).*

64 **GENTLEMAN RABBIT**—This stein was reproduced in the 1950s by R.P.M. and, more recently, by Rastal. (See "Contemporary Steins" CO-38, 71.) The one featured in *ECS* is *not* a Musterschutz stein.

65 **SEATED RAM**—This animal has been redefined in this volume as a *goat*, not a ram. Another version of this stein was made with the goat sitting on a hollow, keg-like base, which was made to support a music box. (See "Animals" AN-47.) It was also made as a pipe. (See "Stein-related Items" SR-47.)*

66 **RAM**—As in the previous stein, we are now calling this animal a goat. This stein was most often seen in the usual beige tones associated with Musterschutz pieces. (See "Animals" AN-48.)*

67 **RAM**—This stein was recently reproduced minus the pewter lid rim by M. Girmscheid. (See "Contemporary Steins" CO-34.)

68 **RAM**—Made by J. W. Remy. (See "Old Catalogs.") This same stein was reproduced after World War II by the same maker.

69 **RAM**—This stein was also made as a large, three-liter master pouring stein. (See "Animals" AN-49.)

71 **WOLF**—This porcelain stein portrays a *bear*, not a wolf. The bear is the symbol of Berlin. Certain regiments had the bear as their symbol, if not as an actual mascot, although this is a distinct possibility. Notice that the snout is much too short to be that of a wolf. The spiked helmet would tend to confirm the army connection. One version of this Musterschutz stein was made in the blue and white "onion" pattern. (See "Animals" AN-4.)*

72 **SITTING RHINOCEROS**—This stein is made of porcelain, not pottery. The German word for rhinoceros is *Nashorn* [literally, nose-horn]. A person who is proud or haughty (stuck-up) is often characterized *hochnaesig* (high-nosed). This stein may very well have been designed as a sly dig at youth, the very condition of which a more mature person might see as arrogant or high-nosed. This would account for the word *Jugend*, "youth" on the scroll.*

73 **RHINOCEROS**—Made by Steinzeugwerke. (See "Old Catalogs.") Another version was made in a light bluish-grey color.

74 **BISON**—The smaller stein on the right was also made with the head of a stag. (See "Miscellaneous" MI-18.) The stein on the left was also made in a ³/₁₀-liter size.

75 **LION**—Probably made by Ernst Bohne.

76 **STAG**—This stein is made of porcelain.*

77 **BOWLING BALL**—This stein was also made in brown wood-grain coloring, probably by H. Hutchenreuter of Probstzella (Thuringia).

78 **BOWLING BALL**—Also made in cream coloring. (See "Athletics" AT-4.)*

79 **BOWLING PIN**—This stein came either with or without a lithophane. It was also available in a cream color or in blue and white

"onion" pattern, as well as in full multicolored front panel. (See "Athletics" AT-3, 5, 6.)*

80   **BOWLING PIN**—Probably made by Steinzeugwerke. Also made in overall cream coloring. (See "Athletics" AT-10.) The German phrases are reversed. It should read: *"Triffst du alle Neun, Darfst du hurra schrein!"* "If you hit all nine, then victory is thine!"

81   **BOWLING PIN**—Made by Steinzeugwerke. The correct height is 15½″ not 13″. It was also made with a different front panel scene either in the brown wood-grain color or in a solid overall cream coloring. (See "Athletics" AT-12, 13, 14.)

82   **BOWLING PIN**—Also made with a simple thumblift.

83   **BOWLING PIN**—Made by J. W. Remy. (See "Old Catalogs.")

84–85   **BOWLING PINS**—These are both the same steins, made by Steinzeugwerke. (See "Old Catalogs.") It also came in an overall cream color. (See "Athletics" AT-9.)

86   **BOWLING PIN**—Made by Steinzeugwerke.

88–89   **BOWLING**—Made by Steinzeugwerke. (See "Old Catalogs.")

90   **BOWLING PIN**—The stein illustrated is actually ³⁄₁₀-liter in size, not ½-liter. It was also made in the brown wood-grain color (See "Athletics" AT-8.)*

91–93   **BOWLING PIN**—Made by Reinhold Merkelbach. (See "Old Catalogs.") It was also made minus the small medallions in the small circles. Other versions of this stein show the three scenes transposed in different panels.

94   **BOWLING**—Probably made by Steinzeugwerke. Another version was made without the pewter rim on the lid.

95   **BOWLING**—Probably made by Steinzeugwerke. Also made in a one-liter size. (See "Athletics" AT-17.) The word *"Lieb"* should be *"Leib."* Translated correctly it would read "Bowling frees both body and soul; it truly makes a sick man whole."

97   **FOOTBALL**—Also made as a lidless mug.

98   **FOOTBALL**—Also made as a lidless pitcher.

100   **FOOTBALL**—This stein has the Princeton University seal on the reverse side. Also made as a 2-liter master pouring stein (see "Athletics" AT-20), and as a lidless mug.

101   **FOOTBALL**—The Columbia University seal is on the reverse side of this stein. (See "Athletics" AT-28.)

102   **FOOTBALL**—The Harvard University seal is on the reverse side of this stein. (See "Athletics" AT-29.)

103   **FOOTBALL**—The Yale University seal is on the reverse side of this stein. (See "Athletics" AT-30.) It was also made as a lidless mug.

104   **FOOTBALL**—The University of Pennsylvania seal is on the reverse side of this stein. (See "Athletics" AT-31.) It was also made as a lidless mug and as a tobacco jar. (See "Stein-related Items" SR-3.)

105   **FOOTBALL**—Also made as a lidless mug.

109   **FOOTBALL**—Also made in orange/brown coloring.

110   **FOOTBALL**—This stein was probably made for Harvard University.

111   **BARBELL**—Probably made by Steinzeugwerke. The lid is a special weight called a kettle bell. This stein was also made in an overall grey

coloring instead of cream. (See "Athletics" AT-1, 2.)

112 **WEIGHTS**—This stein is in the shape of a kettle bell. It was made by Steinzeugwerke. (See "Old Catalogs.") One kilogram is the equivalent of 2.2 pounds. Therefore, 25 kilograms would be 55 pounds, not 11½ pounds.

113 **GOLF BALL**—The stein photographed is actually not a golf ball, but is simply art nouveau designed and made by Reinhold Merkelbach.

114 **DIE**—Made by Steinzeugwerke. (See "Old Catalogs.")

115 **SOCCER BALL**—This stoneware stein was made by Steinzeugwerke. (See "Old Catalogs.") It was also made in an overall cream coloring. (See "Athletics" AT-34.) A newer soccer-ball stein was made recently by M. Girmscheld (See "Contemporary Steins" CO-36.)

116 **LAWN TENNIS**—Probably made by Steinzeugwerke. Art suggests a better translation should read "The noble game of tennis brings joy, but never menace," "Oh game of tennis, noble sport, we'll worship you on every court."

117 **EAGLE**—This same stein was also made in a ³⁄₁₀-liter size. (See "Birds" BD-8.)

118 **EAGLE**—This stein was made without any pewter mountings. The lid rests directly on the stein base and can lift right off.

119 **OWL**—This Mettlach stein is made of stoneware.

120 **OWL WITH JESTER CAP**—One version has been seen with the cap in brown and white coloring. (See "Birds" BD-3.) It was also made in a blue and white coloring. Refer to *Prosit*, no. 33 (December 1973), "Owls on Steins" by Arthur Maethner.*

121 **OWL**—Probably made by Ernst Bohne.

122 **OWL**—This is a new stein and is still being made by M. Girmscheid. (See "Contemporary Steins" CO-27.) This is a copy of an older version, but none have been seen with a Thewalt mark. It was also made in green or various shades of brown.

123 **OWL**—This stein was made by Steinzeugwerke. (See "Old Catalogs.") The correct mold number is 999, not 666. (Hanke was part of Steinzeugwerke.)

124 **EAGLE OWL**—Made by Marzi & Remy. It was also made in a 1-liter and ½-liter size. (See "Birds" BD-7.)

125 **EAGLE OWL**—Made by Marzi & Remy. (See "Old Catalogs.") The stein shown is a ½-liter size, not one liter.

127 **OWL**—This stein carries the HR #1 mark (21a). It is sometimes found without an HR mark.

130 **ROOSTER**—This stein is made out of Majolica, not stoneware, and has been seen with a mark that indicates it was made by Max Heider & Sons of Schongau, Bavaria.

131–138 **"BISMARK"** should be spelled **"Bismarck."**

132 **BISMARCK**—This stein was also made in either full color or in blue and white. (See "Famous People" FP-3, 4, 5.) It also has been copied recently by Rastal in the cream coloring. (See "Contemporary Steins" CO-38.) It was also made in color as a tobacco jar. (See "Stein-related Items" SR-16.) An exact miniature was made as a pipe. (See "Stein-related Items" SR-48.) None of these versions has ever been reported with a lithophane.*

134	**BISMARCK**—This is a post–World War II stein made by a variety of manufacturers. Some carry the R.P.M. mark, some are marked with a black or dark tic-tac-toe mark, and others are unmarked. Some of the ones with the tic-tac-toe mark came in the beige color, others in full color. The full-colored versions varied greatly as they were hand painted. (See "Contemporary Steins" CO-38, 72.)
135	**BISMARCK**—FR stands for *Fridericus Rex*, which is the Latin for Frederick the King, although in history he was known as Frederick the Great. According to Ron Fox this stein was made by the American firm of Whites of Utica.
136	**BISMARCK RADISH**—This stein was also made in a ³⁄₁₀-liter size. *ECS-264* is the same stein.*
137	**STANDING BISMARCK**—This same stein base was also used with the head of Frederich III, only in a dark coloring.
139	**FREDERICH III**—This same stein base has been seen with the head of Wilhelm I.
140	**FREDERICH III**—This *is* a Musterschutz stein. Just before 141 note the following: In the Introduction to Jahn: Friedrich Ludwig Jahn came to be known as the father of gymnastics *(Turnvater)* in the German-speaking areas of central Europe. The first of the four "F's" should be spelled *Frisch*, not *Frish*.
141	**JAHN**—Another variation of this stein depicts Father Jahn wearing a cap. The bodies of the steins are identical, only the lids are different. (See "Famous People" FP-15.)*
142	**JAHN**—This 1-liter stein also came in the traditional beige tones familiar to Musterschutz pieces. (See "Famous People" FP-16, 17.)*
143	In the description about King Ludwig of Bavaria, a better description of Ludwig would be "eccentric" rather than infamous. Also there is no such thing as "most unique." The word *Fussen* should be spelled *Fuessen.*
143	**KING LUDWIG**—This stein also came in a very large size, almost 2 liters in capacity.
143A	**UNCLE SAM**—This stein is made of porcelain. The one illustrated is in full color featuring red, white, and blue. Both the full colored version and the beige version are featured in "Famous People" (FP-1, 2). Some of these steins were probably made prior to 1900. One version has been seen with a wider hat band with three rows of stars instead of two.*
145	**VON MOLTKE**—In the introduction paragraph to the von Moltke section, technically, Wilhelm 1 of Prussia was proclaimed German Emperor *(Deutscher Kaiser)* not Emperor of Germany. The Blue Max or *Pour le merite* was established in 1740 by Frederick the Great.
146	**VON MOLTKE**—This stein was also made by Reinhold Hanke, mold #585. (See "Old Catalogs.") It was also made in an overall cream coloring. (See "Famous People" FP-14.)
149	**WILHELM I**—Made by Marzi & Remy, mold #809. (See "Old Catalogs.") It was also made in blue/grey stoneware. (See "Famous People" FP-8.)
150	**WILHELM II**—One version of this stein has been seen in full color. (See "Famous People" FP-6.) It was also made as a tobacco jar with a different helmet as the lid. (See "Stein-related Items" SR-18.)*

151	**WILHELM II**—Another version of this stein shows the same figure with a full beard, probably Frederich III.
153–154	**TIPSY CAVALIER**—This stein should be retitled *Falstaff*, the fat, merry, ribald, and boastful knight in Shakespeare's *Henry IV, Parts I and II*, and in the *Merry Wives of Windsor*. This is *not* a Musterschutz stein. One version has been seen with the word "BAVARIA" stamped on to its base.
155	**CAVALIER**—This was also made in ½-liter size.
156	**CAVALIER**—This stein was also made in an overall blue coloring. Another version was made as a large master pouring stein. (See "Figurals" FI-54.)
157	**TEUTONIC WARRIOR**—Probably made by Steinzeugwerke. It was also made in full color. (See "Figurals" FI-16.) The text was taken from an old *German* (not Germanic) drinking song, one popular among the *Korporation* of the universities. It refers to the Teutonic warriors of the period from A.D. 50 to 200. Tacitus wrote of his encounters with the Teutons (Germanic tribes), but not with the Germans (a modern designation). Refer to *Prosit*, no. 45 (September 1976), "Schlitt Murals in Wiesbaden."
158	**MUSHROOM MAN**—This *is* a Musterschutz stein. It is interesting to note that the mushroom had the same sort of reputation as a bearer of good fortune as the piglet. The term *Glueckspilz*, "lucky mushroom" means lucky fellow.*
160	**MUSHROOM LADY**—This stein is made of porcelain.*
161	**TURKISH MAN**—This stein has been retitled "Turkish Peasant" in this book. One version of this Musterschutz stein has been seen in full color. (See "Figurals" FI-1.) A copy of this stein has recently been reproduced in ceramic with much less detail. (See "Contemporary Steins" CO-85, 86.) The Musterschutz version was made also as a tobacco jar. (See "Stein-related Items" SR-13.)*
162	**OLD SEA CAPTAIN**—Another version of this stein was made with his pipe reversed in his hand: the bowl by his thumb, the stem between his fingers.*
163	**BURGERMEISTER**—(Should be Buergermeister.) Also made as a tobacco jar. (See "Stein-related Items" SR-11, 12.)
164	**SLEEPING MAN**—This stein has been retitled "Sleeping Hunter" in this book. It is *not* a Musterschutz stein. One version has been seen in full color. (See "Figurals" FI-3, 5.)
165	**ALPINE MAN**—This stein has been retitled "Alpine Mountaineer" in this book. One version has been seen in full color. (See "Figurals" FI-4.) It is doubtful that M. Pauson decorated this or any other stein as they were probably a distributor, not a decorator nor a manufacturer. This stein has also been made as a tobacco jar. (See "Stein-related Items" SR-14.) It was also copied recently in earthenware with much less detail. (See "Contemporary Steins" CO-87, 88, 89.)*
166	**DUTCH BOY**—This Musterschutz stein was also made in the blue and white coloring. (See "Figurals" FI-7.) A newer variation of the blue/white version was made as a bank. (See "Stein-related Items" SR-31, 32, 33.) The Dutch Girl was also made in the blue/white coloring (FI-7).*
167	**BARMAID**—This female figure looks more like a "lady of the evening" than a barmaid.*

168–169	**TYROLEAN MAN & WOMAN**—A similar pair of steins were made marked "Jos. M. Mayer, München" (See "Figurals" FI-62, 63, 64.)
170	**RADISH LADY**—This stein was also made in a ⁴/₁₀-liter size.*
172	**BABY IN BUNTING**—Also made in ³/₁₀-liter size by Ernst Bohne (2).
173	**GOOSEMAN OF NUREMBERG**—This *is* a Musterschutz stein.*
175	**GOOSEMAN OF NUREMBERG**—This stein was made in full color with a bisque finish. (See "Figurals" FI-50.)
176	**MAID GRINDING COFFEE**—In the description, *Kathreiner's Kneipp Malzkaffee* refers to Catherine's Restaurant Malt Coffee. There is no reference there whatsoever to *children*, even though the coffee may be free of caffeine.
181	**ELF**—The correct D.R.G.M. number should be 154927 for this stein.
182	**INDIAN CHIEF**—This is a post–World War II stein probably made by the same maker as the Bartender Pig (*ECS-52*). It is sometimes seen with the Dresden Art mark (36).
183	**MAN**—This hobo-like man has all the indications of being made by Ernst Bohne.
184	**SNOWMAN**—This stein is most often seen in full color rather than in blue/white. It appears to be a snowman rather than a penguin. (See "Figurals" FI-40.)*
185	**MONEYBAGS**—Probably made by H. Hutchenreuter of Probstzella (Thuringia).
186	**CHARLIE WEAVER**—This stein is made of stoneware, not porcelain. The comedian Cliff Arquette did not really copy this character as he was disheveled, and the stein photographed is well dressed. I think the title is incorrect.
187	**END MAN IN A MINSTREL SHOW**—Every copy of this stein we have ever seen has been made of earthenware, not pottery. Therefore, none were made with lithophanes. They all have a very high glaze.
188	**BLACK MAN**—This stein is made of earthenware, not porcelain. Note the similarity to the left stein in *ECS-225*.
190	**HEIDELBERG STUDENT**—The stein on the left is made of stoneware, while the one on the right is made of porcelain. The porcelain version has been copied in the 1950s by R.P.M., and most recently by Rastal. (See "Contemporary Steins" CO-38.) Even though some carry a dark blue crosshatch mark, it is *not* a Musterschutz stein. Many knowledgeable steinologists even believe that all of the porcelain versions are post World War II.
192	**FUNNEL MAN**—Another version was made with a different German verse. (See "Figurals" FI-56, 57.)
195	**LANDLORD**—This is *not* a Musterschutz stein.
197	**MANDARIN MAN**—The word "Man" is redundant. (See explanation in 199). Made by Reinhold Hanke. (See "Old Catalogs.") This base can be found with many different lids.
198	**SMILING CHINAMAN**—We should not use the word Chinaman. This is considered an offensive and patronizing term. A better title might be "Smiling Chinese Man." It was probably made by Reinhold Hanke. Note that this base also is used with many different lids.

199	**MANDARIN WOMAN**—There was no such thing as a Mandarin Woman. Mandarin, in itself, means a man who is a member of the nine ranks of high public officials in Imperial China. A better title might be "Chinese Woman" for this stein. It has been identified as having been made by Reinhold Hanke. (See "Old Catalogs.") Note the similarity in the bases of this and 198 plus others in this book.
201	**RICH MAN**—This stein is a representation of John Bull, a personification of England or the English. Thewalt recently rereleased this stein minus the pewter lid rim and with a ball thumblift. It also lacks the detail of the original. (See "Contemporary Steins" CO-75.) Some versions of the original carry the word MUSTERSCHUTZ incised into the base.
202	**RICH MAN**—This was also made in an overall cream coloring. A female mate can be found in the "Figurals" of this book (see FI-73).
204	**MAN**—This stein carries the HR #1 mark. (21a).
205	**MAN**—Made by Marzi & Remy. (See "Old Catalogs.") Another version has been seen without the pipe in his hand and with a different necktie as mold #804. One was also made in cream and black coloring.
206	**BEER BARREL MAN**—*Gut Heil* does not mean Good Health. It means "Hail to Goods" or "Good Things." The correct name of the actor who played the Great Gildersleave was Harold Perry. The lid rim inscription on this stein reads 1898.
207	**BEER BARREL MAN**—This is a special edition of *ECS-206* in an overall blue coloring.
208	**MAN**—Made of earthenware.
209	**WOMAN**—Made of earthenware.
210	**WOMAN**—Made of earthenware.
211–212	**MAN AND WOMAN**—Many lids are loose on this type of steins and whether they were made this way on purpose is doubtful.
213–214	**MAN AND WOMAN**—The same holds true on these two steins as in 211–212. They have been rereleased recently by Thewalt using mold numbers 9004 for the man and 9005 for the woman. (See "Contemporary Steins" CO-74, 75.)
215	**RICH MOTHER-IN-LAW**—This stein was made by Reinhold Merkelbach. (See "Old Catalogs.") The correct translation should read "This is the dearest mother-in-law." Dearest is used here in the sense of most beloved, esteemed, valued. Note the play on words in that "the most valued" could refer to the money she is carrying. She is held in such high regard because of her wealth. Most copies of this stein have simple bases minus the music box.
217	**FIREMAN**—The *F* on his uniform stands for *Feuerwehrmann* which means "Fireman."
218	**MINER**—Made by Reinhold Merkelbach. (See "Old Catalogs.") The phrase *Glueck auf!* simply means "Good luck." This phrase is the traditional phrase used by miners throughout the German-speaking lands whenever they descend the mineshaft.
219	**BARMAID**—Another version of this stein was made in blue/grey stoneware minus the base by Reinhold Hanke. They both carry the same mold number. (See "Figurals" FI-74.) It is called Kellerin in the original catalog.
220	**NIGHT WATCHMAN**—The weapon held by this figure is called a Halberd.

222	**HOBO**—This stein appears to have been made by Duemler & Breiden.
223	**JOLLY FAT LADY**—This stein appears to have been made by Duemler & Breiden.
224	**BARTENDER**—The correct D.R.G.M. number should be 154927, not 154922. The two German phrases are listed in reverse order and should read "Since the steins do still invite us, let them not beckon in vain."
225	**MAN AND WOMAN**—The figure on the left is really a monk, not a woman. It resembles *ECS*-188. Both are made of earthenware.
228	**MAN**—Made by Steinzeugwerke, mold number 1566. (See "Old Catalogs.") This figure is also a portrayal of the "alter Herr," the old fraternity brother who has come back to the university for a visit (probably on festival day). Note the traditional (*Studentenmuetze*), "student cap" and the ribbon over his left shoulder and across his chest. Normally, these ribbons were worn over the right shoulder, reflecting the colors of the *Korporation*, "fraternity."
229	**BARMAID**—Made by Steinzeugwerke. (See "Old Catalogs.")
230	**ROLY-POLY SOLDIER**—Made by Steinzeugwerke. (See "Old Catalogs.")
231	**WOMAN**—Made by Steinzeugwerke. (See "Old Catalogs.")
234	**WOMAN WITH BABY**—This stein is made of stoneware, not porcelain. It was made by Steinzeugwerke. (See "Old Catalogs.")
236	**GAMBRINUS**—This stein was also made as a full figure in ¼-liter size. (See "Figurals" FI-43.)
238	**GAMBRINUS**—Art suggests a better translation would be "Gambrinus is my name, and beer is my fame."
239	**IRON MAIDEN FROM NUREMBERG**—The T.W. probably stood for Theodor Wieseler of Nuremberg. It is doubtful that he was the maker, but was probably the distributor or seller. This figure was also made as a ¼-liter pewter stein. (See "Figurals" FI-75.) The word *Jungfrau* generally refers to a "virgin." It might be more appropriate to use this title "The Iron Virgin of Nuremberg," since no one was able to "embrace" her long enough to change this condition. The translation really should read "I, the old Nuremberg gal, once brought death, but now I help the thirsty quench their thirst."
240	**BAVARIA**—Another version of this stein shows the statue standing on a base with the word "BAVARIA" on it. It was also made minus the pewter lid rim. (See "Figurals" FI-70.) The head of this bronze statue has three windows in her coiffure where tourists can climb the spiral stairs to get a view of the city of Munich.
243	**BEARDED MAN**—This figural appears to be a takeoff of Jack Frost.
244	**LADY WITH BUSTLE**—This stein carries the HR #1 mark (21a). This same stein was made with a wood and pewter base. The lids are identical. (See "Figurals" FI-71.) The parasol does not form the handle; it attaches to it. The hinge is neatly hidden in the top of the umbrella.
245	**LADY WITH BUSTLE**—This stein carries the HR #1 mark (21a).
246	**MEPHISTOPHELES TEMPTING THE MAIDEN**—This version is shown missing the plumed feather on the hat of Mephistopheles. Another version has been seen copperplated.
247	**KNIGHT**—In the translation, the word *gar* does mean "cooked" but more precisely "well-cooked" in the sense that certain meats (pork

particularly) contained bacteria which could be harmful to the consumer unless they were killed through the cooking process. This phrase goes back to the sixteenth and seventeenth centuries, if not earlier.

250   **KNIGHT**—Made of earthenware. The word *Liebeskraft* is misspelled. It should be *Leibeskraft* (the power of the body, not the power of love.)

252   **ADAM AND EVE**—This stein was also made in ¼-liter, ³⁄₁₀-liter and ½-liter sizes. The ³⁄₁₀-liter version is marked 2043 incised on the bottom side of the apple and GESETZLICH GESCHÜTZT in a circle in green on the base. The ³⁄₁₀-liter size was also marked 4/10 L simply by raising the height of the liter mark on the outside of the stein. They are actually the same size. Possibly made by Ernst Bohne (2).

253   **APPLE**—This stein was designed by Richard Riemerschmid for Villeroy & Boch.

254   **CUCUMBER**—The middle cucumber is made by Steinzeugwerke, mold #1588. (See "Old Catalogs.") The cucumber on the left appears to have been made by Ernst Bohne (2).

255   **SAD RADISH**—This stein was made as a mustard jar and as a salt and pepper shaker set. (See "Stein-related Items," SR-29, 30.)*

256   **SAD RADISH**—It was also made in the blue and white coloring in the ½-liter and 3-liter sizes. (See "Heads" HD-26, 27.) It was also made in a ⁴⁄₁₀-liter size.*

257   **HAPPY RADISH**—One version of the ½-liter radish was also made in the blue and white coloring. It was also made in ⅛-liter size.*

262   **HAPPY RADISH**—The word *Schwinge* on the lid could be an exhortation to the drinker (imbiber) to leap, soar, or fly—to be in a sense a "swinger." This interpretation is far more likely than is a reference to the artist. Generally an artist's signature is found on an obscure portion of the stein so as to not interfere with the piece.

264   **BISMARK RADISH**—Should be "Bismarck Radish." This is the same stein as *ECS*-136 and is made of porcelain. It was also made in a ³⁄₀-liter size.*

265   **ACORN**—This stein was also made in an overall cream coloring.

266   **EAR OF CORN**—This piece is probably a syrup pitcher, not a stein.

267   **SULKY RACE HORSE DRIVER**—Art Maethner believes that this figural stein is actually a masked auto racer, not a sulky driver. It was also made in a ³⁄₁₀-liter and a one-liter size, probably by Ernst Bohne. (See "Heads" HD-3.)

268   **GENTLEMAN SCHOOL TEACHER**—This *is* a Musterschutz stein.*

271   **TYROLEAN MAN**—This Charlie Weaver-looking character stein is probably made by Ernst Bohne.

272   **JUDGE**—Even though the handle of this Musterschutz stein is not shown, I would doubt that his hair is braided. Judges did wear their hair in a pigtail *(zopf)* at one time, but the hair was never braided. This was a device used by peasant women and girls. (Gretl in the Grimm fairy tale, for example) Also see *Prosit* article "Nürnberg Funnel Steins" by Frank L. Love (August 1973, page 184) This stein is

occasionally seen with a white funnel lid. This simply means that the silver has worn off.*

273　**FISHERMAN**—This stein was also made in a ½-liter size, with a different facial expression. (See "Heads" HD-21.) They were probably made by Ernst Bohne.

274　**INDIAN CHIEF**—Both sizes were also made as tobacco jars. The smaller version was also made as a cigar holder. (See "Stein-related Items" SR-42.)

275　**CHINESE MAN**—This stein was also made in ½-liter size.

276　**ORIENTAL MAN**—This stein is made of porcelain, not pottery. The word *Yerehrer* is misspelled. It should be *Verehrer*.

277　**ORIENTAL MAN**—Notice here too that *zopf* is a pigtail and not a braid. Hence, "He wears his pigtail with love and pride," "He suffered in Taku and nearly died."

279　**STUDENT DUELIST**—Bruder Karamozov is most likely the distributor or seller, not the maker.

285　**BLACK MAN**—This *is* a Musterschutz stein.*

288　**HOPS LADY**—This stein has also been seen in the blue and white coloring. (See "Heads" HD-4.) The beige version has recently been copied by Rastal. (See "Contemporary Steins" CO-38.) It was also made as a tobacco jar. (See "Stein-related Items" SR-26.) The stein was also made in ⁴⁄₁₀-liter size.*

289　**HOPS LADY**—Made by Steinzeugwerke. (See "Old Catalogs.") It was also made as a tobacco jar with a matching stoneware lid. (See "Stein-Related Items" SR-25.)

290　**EGYPTIAN LADY**—There are actually two versions of this stein. The one photographed in *ECS* is a cruder, and probably later version. The original has much better detail. They are both shown together in the "Heads" chapter of this book (HD-10).

291　**COQUETTE**—This stein was originally identified as J. W. Remy. It was recently made by M. Girmscheid minus the pewter lid rim and in bright colors. (See "Contemporary Steins" CO-26.) She also had a mate #765. (See "Heads" HD-23.)

292　**CAROLINE**—This Musterschutz stein was also made as a tobacco jar. (See "Stein-related Items" SR-24.) A stoneware version was also made. (See "Heads" HD-12.)*

293　**SMILING WOMAN**—A better full color photo of this stein can be seen in the "Heads" chapter of this book (HD-5).

294　**MASQUERADE LADY**—This stein could well be a portrayal of the main female lead in the Johann Strauss operetta *Die Fledermaus* "The Bat" which features several magnificent masked balls.*

295–296　**BLACK GIRL AND BLACK BOY**—Both of these pieces are actually tobacco jars that were recently made into steins. They were never made originally as steins.

302　**FOOTBALL MAN**—The title appears to be incorrect. The figure shown is actually that of a student's head. It was made by Rosskopf & Gerz and appears in their 1914 catalog. (See "Old Catalogs.")

304　**PAN**—This stein has no pewter mountings, the lid just lifts off. One version has been seen with a fancy silver lid. Pan was the Greek god of woods, fields, and flocks, having a human torso with goat's legs, horns, and ears.

305   **PIXIE**—This Musterschutz stein was also made as a tobacco jar.*

307   **JUDGE**—One version of this stein has been seen in the blue and white "onion" pattern. (See "Clowns and Jesters" CL-1.) Also see *Prosit* article "Nürnberg Funnel Steins" by Frank L. Love (August 1973, p. 184).*

309   **CLOWN WITH BANJO**—In the second line of verse the word *leid* actually means "suffering" not "song." The phrase now makes more sense as "in sorrow and life strive for unity."

311   **MAN WITH JESTER'S HAT**—The correct D.R.G.M. number should be 154927, not 154327. They also made a matching ¼-liter mate to complete the set. (See "Clowns and Jesters" CL-8.)

312   **MAN WITH JESTER'S HAT**—This stein was also made as a set with a matching ¼-liter stein (See "Clowns and Jesters" CL-11.)

313   **JESTER**—The correct D.R.G.M. number should be 154927.

314   **CLOWN**—Another version of this stein was made with a fancy cap. (See "Clowns and Jesters" CL-10.)

316   **CLOWN**—Also made in blue/grey stoneware. (See "Clowns and Jesters" CL-15.)

317   **CLOWN**—Probably made by Steinzeugwerke.

320   **CLOWN**—This stein was also made as a miniature ⅛-liter in cream coloring minus the pewter attachments. (See "Clowns and Jesters" CL-12.)

321   **WOMAN WITH JESTER'S HAT**—Another version of this stein was made with her hair forming the lid instead of a jester's hat.

322   **MILITARY HEAD**—It is interesting to note that the word *Raupe* means "caterpillar," hence the colloquial expression "caterpillar" helmet.

324–325   **ENLISTED MAN**—This stein was used often and decorated according to the colors of the reservist's unit. Two other versions can be found in the "Military" chapter of this book (see MT-4, 5). Also, the *K* in both the words *Kurassier* and *Koller* should be capitalized.

327   **GERMAN OFFICER**—Made by Merkelbach & Wick, mold #381. Another version with the Merkelbach & Wick mark has been seen with the same lid, but with the body similar to Wilhelm I in "Famous People" of this book.

332   **SAILOR**—This stein has recently been made by Thewalt, mold #9006. (See "Contemporary Steins" CO-77.)

333   **ARTILLERY SHELL**—This stein has been seen with different color timing bands. It was also made with various lithophanes. I have even seen one that was made into a regimental stein.

334   **ARTILLERY SHELL**—This stein came in different colors and lithophanes. (See "Military" MT-10.)

335   **ARTILLERY SHELL**—This stein also came with blue pressure bands. It was also made with "1914/15" on the lid. (See "Military" MT-9.)

339   **MONK**—This stein also was made with a bronze lid. (See "Monks and Nuns" MO-5.)

344   **GRINNING MONK**—This stein was also made in full color. (See "Monks and Nuns" MO-8.)

351   **GRINNING MONK**—Made by Reinhold Hanke. (See "Old Catalogs.") Note the same base is used on the Nun (*ECS*-363).

352	**MONK**—Probably made by Gilles & Sohn. The mate to this stein can be found in the "Munich Child" chapter of this book (MC-33).
353	**MONK**—Made by Steinzeugwerke.
354	**MONK**—This stein was made with many different lithophanes. The same base is used on the Nun (*ECS*-365).
356	**MONK**—Made by Marzi & Remy, mold #716. (see "Old Catalogs.")
358	**MONK**—This stein has been reproduced recently with a simple thumblift.
360	**MONK**—A similar ¼-liter stein has been made as a mate. (See "Monks and Nuns" MO-10.)
361	**NUN**—Made by Marzi & Remy. The same stein base was made with a monk's head as a lid.
363	**NUN**—Made by Reinhold Hanke and by Steinzeugwerke. (See "Old Catalogs.") The size should be ½-liter, not ¼-liter.
364	**NUN**—A companion monk stein with the same body was also made. (See "Monks and Nuns" MO-13.) Note *ECS*-366 has the same stein body.
365	**NUN**—This stein was made with many different lithophanes. This is the mate to *ECS*-354. It was also made in an overall brown coloring.
366	**NUN**—This is the same stein as *ECS*-364 except for the bronze lid and the rust/red body coloring.
368	**MUNICH CHILD**—A newer version of this stein was made in 1976 by Rastal in both ½-liter and ¼-liter sizes. (See "Contemporary Steins" CO-39, 41, 42.)
369	**MUNICH CHILD**—Also made in ⅛-liter size. (See "Munich Child" MC-45.)
370	**MUNICH CHILD**—This stein has been identified as having been made by Reinhold Merkelbach, mold #1. (See "Old Catalogs.") This stein appears to go with *ECS*-387, and with a ¼-liter version found in the "Munich Child" section of this book (MC-37).
371	**MUNICH CHILD**—This stein is very seldom seen with the wooden tankard. It was also made in a 1-liter size, moldmarked #1238.
372	**MUNICH CHILD**—The wording on the bottom of this stein actually reads *Munchner Kindl*, not *Muncher Kindl*. Another ¼-liter version shows her holding a stein and a bunch of radishes. (See "Munich Child" MC-18.)
373	**MUNICH CHILD**—Another version of this stein shows her holding a beer stein in one hand and radishes in the other. (See "Munich Child" MC-21.)
374	**MUNICH CHILD**—These steins were also made in porcelain in some of the sizes. The stoneware versions came in five sizes: ¹⁄₁₆ liter, ⅛ liter, ¼ liter, ½ liter, and 1 liter. Also there is some doubt that Reinemann was a decorator. It is believed that they were merely the distributors or sellers. Many of them do not carry the Reinemann name.
376	**MUNICH CHILD**—There are many different variations of this stein, some marked, some unmarked. They range in size from ⅛ liter to 1½ liters. (See "Munich Child" MC-28.)
379	**MUNICH CHILD**—This stein was also made in ¼-liter and ½-liter sizes and marked "Jos. M. Mayer München."

380	**MUNICH CHILD**—These steins were made in either rust/brown or black. Many of these steins have been made after World War II. Some stein experts believe that many of them are of recent vintage. They range in size from ⅛ liter to ½ liter. (See "Munich Child" MC-12.)
383	**MUNICH CHILD**—Made by Steinzeugwerke. (See "Old Catalogs.")
385	**MUNICH CHILD**—A matching ¼-liter stein was made to go along with this master stein, possibly as a set. (See "Munich Child" MC-23.)
386	**MUNICH CHILD**—Also made in a ½-liter size. It is believed that Reinemann was a distributor, not a decorator.
387	**MUNICH CHILD**—Made by Reinhold Merkelbach. This is a mate to *ECS*-370 and to a ¼-liter version shown in this book. The phrase, "down at the Platze" could be translated as "down on the square." The Munichers should be "citizens of Munich."
390	**MUNICH CHILD**—A similar stein was made in blue/grey stoneware minus the pewter lid rim. (See "Munich Child" MC-52.)
392	**MUNICH CHILD**—Made by Steinzeugwerke. Also made in a ½-liter size.
393	**MUNICH CHILD**—Made by Steinzeugwerke. (See "Old Catalogs.")
394	**MUNICH CHILD**—Another version of this stein shows her holding a holy book in her left hand instead of radishes. (See "Munich Child" MC-24, 25.) The marking *Reichs Zinn* means "Federally Approved Pewter."
396–397	**BARREL**—These steins also came with a fish handle. *ECS*-396 also was made with a spigot on the smaller barrel on the lid. A custom version of *ECS*-397 can be seen in the "Munich Child" chapter of this book (MC-1).*
398	**BARREL**—This is probably a Musterschutz stein.*
399	**MUNICH CHILD**—The "JRM" on the pewter hinge pin might stand for J. Reinemann, Munich. A miniature version can be seen in this book (MC-48).
400	**SKULL ON BOOK**—Another version was made by Schierholz. (See "Skulls and Satans" SK-9, 10.)
401	**SKULL ON BOOK**—This ½-liter was reproduced in 1955. It was available with either an inlay lid or pewter lid. They were marked "Made 1955" and retailed for $9.95 when advertised in the April 1956 issue of *Hobbies* magazine. Another newer version can be seen in "Contemporary Steins" (CO-91, 92). One of the original steins has been seen with a green book and with the Ernst Bohne (2c) mark.
406	**SKULL**—Some versions of this stein have been seen with a military scene on the inside of the lid. The "soldier" depicted on this skull is actually a cavalryman, a Hussar, a member of a light cavalry regiment having dress uniforms of ultimately Hungarian style, typically with much bragging. They were known in Germany as the "Death's Head Hussars" or the *Totenkopf Husaren* because they wore a death's head (or skull) on their elaborate headgear. (See *Prosit* article "The 17th Totenkopf (death head) Hussars," June 1976, p. 333.) This same stein was made in stoneware instead of porcelain.
407	**BACK TO BACK SKULLS**—This stein was made of porcelain, not pottery. It was made by Ernst Bohne and carries their (2a) mark.
408–9–10	**HALF SATAN-HALF SKULL**—This stein is made of bisque porcelain.

412	**SATAN**—Number 4708 is sometimes incised into the base.
414	**SATAN**—This stein has a replaced pewter lid that was meant to be used on a pouring stein. The correct lid is made of stoneware similar to *ECS-415*.
416	**DUERERTURM TOWER**—This same stein was made in a ⅛-liter size with a matching stoneware lid. (See "Towers" TO-3.) F&M/N has been identified as Felsenstein & Mainzer of Nuremberg. They only made pewter pieces, so they probably had these stoneware steins made for them by another maker. Hans Sachs, not Hans Sach, was one of Old Nuremberg's most famous residents. He was a poet, a dramatist, and a Meistersinger (immortalized by Richard Wagner in his opera "Die Meistersinger von Nürnberg").
	We will be using the English reference as Nuremberg instead of the German Nürnberg, and Duererturm Tower instead of Dürerturm Tower.
417	**TOWER**—This Duererturm Tower also was made in a ½-liter size. They also were made and marked the same as *ECS-416*. (See "Towers" TO-1, 2.)
418	**TOWER**—This Duererturm Tower was made by Felsenstein & Mainzer. There have been many smaller versions of this pewter tower as they were sold as souvenirs of the city. The interior of this stein is usually a shinier pewter than the exterior. It is doubtful, though, that it was silverplated.
419	**FRAUENKIRCHE TOWER**—The spelling should be *Frauenkirchenturm*, "the tower of the church of our dear lady." The T.W. probably stands for Theodor Wieseler of Nuremberg who was the distributor of the stein, not the maker. (A smaller ¼-liter size was also made. (See "Towers" TO-15.) Both sizes were recently copied by Rastal in both stoneware and porcelain. (See "Contemporary Steins" CO-40.)
420	**FRAUENKIRCHE TOWER**—(see above). This stein was also made in a 1-liter size. The lid is also made of porcelain.
421	**ST. PETER'S CHURCH**—For more information on this stein see *Prosit* article "St. Peter's Stein" by Walt Rippert (December 1976, p. 376).
424	**CASTLE TOWER**—This stein was also made with turrets on either side of the balcony. It also was made in a ½-liter size. (See "Towers" TO-17, 18.)
425–6	**CLOCK TOWERS**—Both steins were made by J. W. Remy. (See "Old Catalogs.") The one in color on the right is a post–World War II stein. The detail on this reproduction is much cruder than the original shown on the left.
427	**TOWER**—This tower has been seen with a continuous porcelain lid that forms the roof. It has been identified as the East Berlin City Hall. (See "Towers" TO-11.)
428	**WRAP AROUND ALLIGATOR**—This stein was probably made by Ernst Bohne. It was also made in a ³⁄₁₀-liter size, and as a tobacco jar. (See "Stein-related Items" SR-4.)
429	**SITTING ALLIGATOR**—This stein was also made in a ½-liter size minus the music box base. (See "Old Catalogs.")
430	**SITTING ALLIGATOR**—A miniature version of this stein was also made but with much less detail. Another miniature version was made

as a salt shaker. (See "Stein-related Items" SR-2.)*

431   **FISH**—This stein has been reproduced recently by A. J. Thewalt Co. The newer version has no music box base and is an overall green coloring rather than the grey color of the original. It was also made minus a pewter lid rim.

432   **FROG**—One version has been seen with the words "St. Augustine" on the frog's belly.*

434   **HEIDELBERG FROG DUELIST**—This is *not* a Musterschutz stein. Another version was made in full color. The *Frosch*, "frog" is used by members of the *Korporation*, "fraternities" to denote an initiate to the society.

435   **FROG**—One version of this stein depicts the frog standing on a book which is meant to hold a music box. (See "Water Animals" WA-3.) It was probably made by Ernst Bohne.

436   **FROG AS ROMAN COMMANDER-IN-CHIEF**—Actually, this stein looks more like a creature from space than a frog. The medallions on his chest seem to indicate this.

437   **GENTLEMAN FROG**—This stein was made in January 1980 by M. Girmscheid minus the pewter lid rim, mold #836. (See "Contemporary Steins" CO-33.) Art suggests a better translation would be "If you do not wish to flounder in the swamp as frogs are want to do, ascend to the realm of Gambrinus to enjoy full mugs of brew." The original was made by J. W. Remy (39).

438   **FROG**—This stein was also made in an overall cream coloring. (See "Water Animals" WA-2.)

439   **FROG**—This is a post–World War II stein made by M. Girmscheid. (See "Contemporary Steins" CO-30.) The translation is "The frog croaks when he takes refreshment (drinks)."

440–441   **HOUSE**—Made by Steinzeugwerke. (See "Old Catalogs.")

442   **HOUSE**—This stein is made of porcelain, not pottery.

443   **PRETZEL**—This stein is made of stoneware, not porcelain. The colorings vary from stein to stein from brown to a light beige tone.

444   **ZUGSPITZE**—There is another stoneware mountain stein that was made in a 1-liter size that has a dragon for a handle. (See "Miscellaneous" MI-19, 20.)

445   **NUREMBERG FUNNEL**—This stein is made of porcelain. An upside-down version, made as a goblet, is seen in the "Stein-related Items" chapter of this book (SR-1). Also see *Prosit* article "Nürnberg Funnel Steins" by Frank L. Love (August 1973, page 184). Other versions of this stein have been seen with a yellowish coloring.*

446   **MARKSMAN**—The word *Schuentzenliesl* is misspelled. It should be *Schuetzenliesl*. The shooting contests or matches were referred to as *Schuetzenfeste*. The word *Schuetzenliesl* refers to the type of girl portrayed in *ECS*-447 and 448. *Liesl* is a shortened form of *Lieselotte*.

449   **KEEPER OF THE WINE**—The figure portrayed on the top of this stein is most certainly that of Perkeo. Compare this figure with *ECS*-227 as well as the drawing of this famous court jester and the photo of the figure itself in front of the wine cask. The lithophane featured is probably the city of Heidelberg.*

453   **TIPSY CAVALIER**—This stein is made of stoneware, not porcelain. It has also been seen with the cavalier in white, and also with a plain lid.

454   **BEEHIVE**—This stein was made by Reinhold Merkelbach. (See "Old Catalogs.") There were actually two different versions made of this stein. One has seventeen bees and the other features twenty bees. The one featured in *ECS* is the seventeen-bees version. Both of them are shown together in the "Miscellaneous" chapter of this book (MI-1). The beehive illustrated in the old catalog shows this stein with a pewter lid.

455   **ROOK**—The chessboard on the lid of this stein actually has holes in the dark squares which were probably meant to hold pegs which represented chess pieces. In fact, one can be seen in this photo.

457   **HOT AIR BALLOON**—This ¾-liter stein was made either in cream and green coloring or in full color. The T.W. could stand for Theodor Wieseler.

458   **BICYCLE**—Another version of this stein features a "cat with a hangover" lid. (See "Animals" AN-19.)*

459   **L.A.W. BICYCLE**—L.A.W. stands for "League of American Wheelmen" not Wheelers. The lid features the official L.A.W. insignia.*

460   **HIGH WHEELER**—The correct date for this type of bicycle should be 1880, not 1860.

462   **ARMORED KNIGHT**—F & M has been identified as Felsenstein & Mainzer of Nuremberg. Another version was made in full color. (See "Miscellaneous" MI-2, 3.)

466   **DRAWSTRING BAG OF MONEY**—The T.W. might stand for Theodor Wieseler of Nuremberg.

BEER STEIN CERAMICS

JACK G. LOWENSTEIN

ALL CERAMICS, ONE MIGHT SAY, ARE "RELATIVES UNDER THE SKIN": THEY ARE ALL MADE OF clay. What causes them to be different are the types of clays utilized, the various additives mixed in, and the temperature at which the formed pieces are fired. At one end of the scale one might place the simple sun-dried earthenware one finds, for example, made by Indians in the Southwest. At the extreme other end of this continuum is porcelain, the most sophisticated and most highly fired of the ceramics. In between would fall such other categories as fired earthenware and stoneware; specialized and regional terms, such as faience, majolica, basalt, fine stoneware, soft paste, etc., are merely synonyms for the basic categories of pottery—albeit they may be differentiated by their glaze treatment, coloration, and mode of forming.

The beer stein collector, and specifically the character stein collector, may restrict himself to just three types of ceramics: earthenware, stoneware, and porcelain. Hence, we will restrict ourselves to discussing these major categories in this brief discourse. We will briefly "define," i.e., describe each type and then by means of a tabular presentation highlight the similarities and differences among them.

In general, once the collector has seen and handled representative examples of the various types of ceramics, he will find it relatively easy to tell one from the other: by weight, thickness of cross section, translucency, glaze, general appearance, and so on. Of course, there are other hints: Lithophanes are always made of porcelain and are always in porcelain steins! On the other hand, not every porcelain stein contains a lithophane in its bottom; so, when there is no lithophane and the finely finished surface is covered with colored glazes, how can one tell? Not easily, as is the case with some "HR" steins where a gaudy exterior hides a porcelain body! So now let us explore the three ceramic types briefly:

A. *Earthenware*—this type of pottery was, for ages, the most common, popular, and plentiful. Earthenware is made of common clays, with various admixtures, which are fired at relatively low temperatures and are consequently not *vitrified*. Vitrification is an important term in ceramics and hence deserves its own definition: A vitrified body has been converted to a glass-like state, i.e., hard, glassy, impermeable (to gases and liquids); this has been accomplished by subjecting it to very high temperatures ("firing") so that the clays, in the presence of "fluxes," start to melt into one another, forming a glass. Although a vitrified body is still crystalline, individual clay particles have lost their identity. To carry the analogy further, consider common glass: Ordinary sea sand is mixed with soda ash and a little borax—all powdery materials which, after they are mixed, are still just white, finely divided particles. But place this mixture in a crucible and heat it to a yellow-white heat, and the sand will begin to fuse with the soda ash (borax acts as the flux) and melt. Upon cooling, we find that a hard, transparent mass has been formed in the crucible: We have made glass! In other words, the material was vitrified. If we were to shatter this glass and pound it into a fine powder, we would indeed have glass crystals, but we will never be able to get our original starting materials (sand, soda ash, and borax) back; they have permanently lost their identity. So it is with other forms of vitrified substances.

Getting back to earthenware; being *non* vitrified, because it was fired at relatively low temperatures (below 1000° C), earthenware is "soft" and permeable. To protect it and to make it watertight, potters developed glazes which would temporarily do what the ceramic alone could not. So the potters of Faienza, Italy, invented a tin oxide glaze which covered the earthenware with a semitransparent, white covering; not only did this "tin glaze" improve the properties of the ceramic piece, it enhanced it since it was a good ground for decorations. And that is why we call this type of pottery "faience" (it is also called "majolica" when multicolored designs are applied, or "delft" when it is decorated in the typical Dutch blue-design fashion). Because common kilns (firing ovens) are unable to reach high temperatures, the so-called hobby glazes were developed. These are mainly lead-based, and we need not discuss these here since these are rarely used on drinking vessels because of the extremely high toxicity of lead. Earthenware, glazed or not, is still quite "soft" and is easily damaged; unless exposed edges are covered with pewter rims, earthenware steins soon are chipped and cracked; indeed, many times holes can be found in old faience bodies. There are a very few earthenware *character* steins; old majolica owls, made in Italy and southern Germany in the seventeenth and eighteenth centuries are probably the best-known examples, although others are present in *ECS* and in this publication. Some "modern," i.e., mid-twentieth century, character steins, notably Japanese, are made of lead-glazed earthenware. They are easily broken, they are rather light in weight, and they are heavily glazed.

In general, then, earthenware character steins would be characterized by their light weight, heavy glazes to strengthen and harden the ceramic base, and—in the case of antique steins—pewter reinforcements. Thickness of the clay body is surprisingly thin—since clay adherence is quite good, despite the lack of vitrification. Once again, this is a very minor fraction of the known character steins.

B. *Stoneware*—here we have reached the first step in the vitrification chain. Realizing that somehow higher firing temperatures made better ceramic pieces, the potters of twelfth- and thirteenth-century Germany, especially those in the Rhine valley, worked diligently to increase their kiln temperatures. By using bellows to blow extra air into the flames, and by experimenting with hotter-burning woods, temperatures in excess of 1200°C were finally reached. And lo, the result was the production of hard, impermeable clay bodies. We don't know whether these ancient potters realized it, but they had succeeded in fusing the clays and silicates at the new high temperatures, and they had vitrified them. This new stoneware was hard enough to scratch steel (we wouldn't recommend experimenting with your favorite stein, however) and impermeable enough to serve as water and sewer pipes, tiles, and, of course, drinking vessels. Techniques were improved in the next seven to eight hundred years, and extremely fine stoneware items were produced. One need only look at the "genealogy" of drinking vessels, from Raeren and Frechen "Schnellen" to Villeroy & Boch's magnificent semi-mass-produced "Krüge" and "Becher," to realize the advances in this art.

Stoneware is characterized by its weight, by its total lack of translucency, by its hardness and by its glassy appearance. Although stoneware need not be glazed to improve its physical characteristics, it was and is often glazed for decorative purposes; thus salt-glaze has been a favorite in Germany, since it imparts a beautiful luster to cobalt-(blue), manganese-(purple) and iron-(yellow and yellow/brown) oxide decorated clay bodies. Salt-glaze is just about what the name implies. When the firing process is at its peak and maximum temperatures have been reached in the kiln, the potter opens up a small hole in the roof of the furnace and shovels in ordinary salt, i.e., sodium chloride. The salt quickly vaporizes at the extreme temperatures and chemically combines with the metallic constituents of the clay; a sodium-metal-silicate complex is formed, another glass one might say, and this covers all exposed surfaces of the ceramic pieces being fired. As a by-product, voluminous quantities of hydrogen chloride are given off, making this process environmentally very unattractive. Modern salt-glazing kilns have to have extensive gas-scrubbing systems to catch the hydrogen chloride and prevent it from escaping to the atmosphere. Since these vent systems are very expensive, salt-glazing may well be disappearing (except, fortunately, where the cost is justified or where the retrofitting has already been accomplished).

Stoneware may also be decorated by every other ceramic decorative technique, from incising to polychroming (multicolored decorations) to relief application to printing or painting under or over the glaze. As a "canvas" for the artist to air his creative and imaginative instincts, stoneware is unexcelled!

Alert collectors have observed that occasionally a "stoneware" stein is found which appears to lack some of the "definition" properties of stoneware: hardness and impermeability. Is such a stein truly stoneware? And if not, what might it be?

Please recall that we stated that stoneware was a vitrified state, i.e., that high firing temperatures had caused a melting together of clays and fluxes. But when most of the steins in which we are interested were produced—about one hundred years ago—temperature measuring devices were crude, and quality control (especially for such menial items as beer steins) was minimal. Hence it was possible that a kiln did not reach full vitrification temperature or did not hold such required temperature for a sufficiently long period of time to completely vitrify the particular clay used (the clay varies from source to source, and even variations in particle size can markedly affect vitrification properties). What was the manufacturer to do—since he couldn't afford to scrap an entire furnace's production? If results were "close" (and the fired items looked good to him), he sold the wares as *Steinzeug*, "stoneware"; if not, he called them *Steingut*, neither stoneware nor earthenware, but an intermediary, partially vitrified ceramic. How can we, so many years later, tell exactly what the material is? We can't, unless we break the stein and test hardness and porosity characteristics, or examine a section under a high-powered microscope. And if we can't tell without such "incursive diagnosis," what should we call this material? Well, we think we should call it "stoneware," namely that which it was intended to be.

We might note that there are some souvenir steins, usually cream or yellow in color, highly glazed, which were purposely made of *Steingut*, because it was less expensive to fire at lower temperatures. These semi-vitrified steins are not as hard as stoneware, they chip and break easily, but can be just as decorative (most are PUG's) as true stoneware steins.

C. *Porcelain*—Tales of a pure white, light, translucent, and hard ceramic were told by seafarers and travelers returning from the Orient as early as the fifteenth century, and rumors of the existence of such a material were whispered about in Europe since before the Renaissance. One can point to a few smuggled pieces, which may have found their way west with Marco Polo, as the motivation for potters and ceramicists all over Europe to try to copy this fine "china." By the sixteenth century, when trade with China and Japan became a major industry, oriental porcelain was more valuable than gold. Royalty outbid each other for choice pieces, and wars were fought over hoards of porcelain. No wonder that kings and queens commissioned their royal ceramicists to duplicate the material. ("Commissioning" may be too gentle a word; "threatening" may be better, since usually the ceramicist's reward for failure to copy porcelain was death.) No need to go into the European history of porcelain; we know that at last Johann Friedrich Boettger, more alchemist than ceramicist, "invented" porcelain in Dresden, Germany, at the very beginning of the eighteenth century (1708). His closely guarded recipes were soon stolen and dispersed throughout Europe. The exquisite material soon was the property of every rich nobleman and lady; commoners had to wait a little longer. What had been the secret, so long kept successfully by the Chinese? Again, the proper combination of clays and fluxes and high firing temperatures, from 1350° to 1500°C.

To reduce the cost of the "real" porcelain, some factories, notably the English, attempted to make vitrified imitations of porcelain by adding bone meal to modified formulas; this "bone china" is also called "soft paste" and was extensively used for dinner services, plates, bowls, and similar articles. Genuine porcelain, or "hard paste," was used for all of these, as well as statuary pieces and decorative items of every description. Tankards were a favorite, again because the material lent itself so well to decorating and because it could be formed with such thin cross sections. One need only look at some of the Dresden and Vienna

Figure 15. Old Jug or Bottle Oven. Was used for many years by the J.W. Remy firm—the oven in which many stoneware character steins, including the clock-tower stein (*ECS-425*), were fired. (Courtesy of Roland Henschen)

Figure 16. Wood-fired kiln in Hoehr-Grenzhausen. This is the typical kiln used for a century or more to fire, vitrify, and glaze stoneware articles.

Figure 18. Small Hoehr-Grenzhausen kiln, after firing operation and partially emptied. Note stacking trays, fired and glazed stein bodies, and brick furnace lining.
(All photographs by Jack G. Lowenstein)

Figure 17. Typical stoneware firing kiln in Hoehr-Grenzhausen, stacked with green (unfired) stoneware bodies.

masterpieces to understand why drinking vessels were always in the forefront of the decorative arts.

Lithophanes were a natural extension of the utilization of this translucent ceramic. And while we do not know whether lithophanes first made their appearance in the bottom of steins, we do know that this is indeed a favorite use. The many porcelain character steins illustrated in this book show the range of the artist's imagination; the lithophanes in so many of them are the "topping on the cake"—even if they are in the bottom of the stein. (See "A Light at the End of the Stein—Lithophanes.")

What characterizes porcelain: a glassy white body, a degree of translucency, extreme hardness, a very fine surface, thin cross sections but a surprisingly heavy weight. Porcelain wares may be glazed or left unglazed. When to be glazed, the unfired body is dipped in a porcelain slip glaze, which is readily absorbed by the "greenware," and fired at high temperature (1350°–1500°C); the result is the shiny, hard surface we associate with fine porcelain dinnerware, figurines, and steins. If unglazed, the body is fired at perhaps slightly lower temperatures (ca. 1350°C), and the result is "bisque" or "biscuit," a nongloss finish which is ideal for special applications in statuary and, luckily for stein collectors, for making very lifelike faces (which would suffer from a high-gloss appearance)—this technique was especially used by Josef Mayer of Munich on his "Munich Child" character steins. It should be remembered that only a very thin line separates porcelain from stoneware, since both are vitrified materials; the difference merely lies in the fineness of the clays and the firing temperatures. Indeed, *Feinsteinzeug*, "fine stoneware" is an intermediate grade of stoneware, smoother, whiter, and "finer" than the usual grades, just slightly inferior to porcelain (since it is not translucent like porcelain and cannot be formed in the very thin sections that porcelain can). Many of the better-made character steins are made of *Feinsteinzeug*.

Well, we have described in general terms what is meant by the three major categories of ceramics: earthenware, stoneware, and porcelain. We have presented a few characteristics, especially those of importance to stein enthusiasts. As stated earlier, the best way to learn the differences and similarities of these materials is to look at, handle, and study representative pieces. This book, with its hundreds of examples, all fully described, will serve handsomely to that end. The libraries have many excellent books on the subject; we won't even list a bibliography here, since any card catalog will have plentiful titles under such headings as "ceramics," "porcelain," "stoneware," "earthenware," "faience," etc. The interested collector should do some reading to familiarize him- or herself with the terms used, with the important aspects of each of the materials, and with the specialized applications related to each. Finally, we have appended a comparative table as a condensed overview of this very complex subject; it will give the reader the chance to distinguish among the major ceramics without having to spend too much time "digging."

Obviously such a tabulation can be only very general and far from complete. We hope that it serves not only as a primer, but as a motivating device to get you, the reader, to study further, to learn more about this fascinating subject, and thereby to enjoy our favorite hobby, beer stein collecting, that much more. Finally, remember: whether you drink out of an earthenware, or a stoneware, or a porcelain stein, the correct toast is always "Prosit!"

Acknowledgment. I am indebted to Roland A. Henschen for reading my original manuscript and for making valid and valuable comments and suggestions. The interested reader is invited to look at the article authored by Roland Henschen and Liselotte Lopez in the December 1975 issue of *Prosit* (the official magazine of Stein Collectors International), pages 306 and 307, entitled "Ceramic Definitions," for thumbnail descriptions of the various types of ceramics.

JGL

A CERAMICS GLOSSARY

JACK G. LOWENSTEIN

THE COLLECTION OF CERAMICS IS BECOMING AN EVER MORE POPULAR HOBBY. AS COLLEC-tors discover the beauty of the potter's work, from the most ancient to modern, from European and Asian to American, so does their zeal for owning more pieces increase. However, it is surprising how few collectors actually know the meaning of many of the terms and names used for various types of pottery: majolica, porcelain, faience, stoneware, bone china—all are used with gay abandon, without too much regard for their actual meaning.

This very brief glossary of terms is intended to define some of the types of "pottery." Only the clay wares themselves are covered, not the decorations, glazes, kiln and firing terms, or the general potter's jargon. For more complete descriptions, consult any good book on ceramics, pottery, or porcelain. But for a concise introduction, start here:

Artificial porcelain	see: Soft paste porcelain.
Basalt ware	black unglazed vitreous stoneware, exemplified by Wedgwood.
Bisque (or Bisquit)	unglazed porcelain.
Blanc-de-Chine	very fine white Chinese porcelain of the Ming period, with a thick, lustrous glaze.
Bone China	English earthenware in which calcined bone ashes were added to the clay. Not really "China."
Bow	see: Soft paste porcelain.
Capo-di-Monte	ornately modeled and well-glazed soft paste porcelain, Italy, mid-eighteenth century.
Chelsea	see: Soft paste porcelain.
China	originally a synonym for Chinese porcelain, but now often (incorrectly) used for any white ware.
Delft ware	see: Earthenware.
Derby	see: Soft paste porcelain.
Dresden	see: Meissen.
Earthenware	non-vitrified pottery, kiln-hardened at 850°–1000°C, porous; the most common type of ceramics, synonymous with "pottery." Usually lead-glazed (hobby and studio pottery, commercial pottery), tin-glazed (faience, delftware, majolica), slip decorated (slipware), or left unglazed (terra cotta).
Faience	tin-glazed earthenware.

45

Hard paste porcelain	true porcelain, made of kaolin (china clay) and petuntse (china stone: feldspathic clay). Fired at 1350°–1500°C, completely vitrified. It is so hard ordinary steel will not cut it. White, translucent, nonporous. Will "ring" when struck. Invented by Chinese in A.D. 600, and was "rediscovered" at Meissen, Germany, in 1708, by either E. von Tschirnhaus or Johann Boettger; first sold commercially in 1713. Found its way into major European countries by mid-eighteenth century. Also called "pâte dure."
Ironstone	hard earthenware body, originally supposed to contain pulverized iron slag. Used for dinnerware, often erroneously called "semi-porcelain." Developed by Josiah Spode in 1805.
Jasper ware	fine-grained tinted stoneware perfected by Josiah Wedgwood in 1775. Used for cameos, relief ware, plaques.
Kreussen	see: Stoneware.
Lenox	American porcelain manufacturer since 1906.
Limoge	French manufacturer of fine porcelain. See: Hard paste porcelain.
Majolica	see: Earthenware.
Meissen	Royal Factory in Germany, near Dresden, where European hard paste porcelain was first developed. The Meissen factories spread throughout the Dresden area, are still famed for their work. See: Hard paste porcelain.
Nonvitrified	porous, relatively soft (i.e., can be scratched with steel) clayware, fired at low temperatures. See: Earthenware.
Pâte dure	see: Hard paste porcelain.
Pâte tendre	see: Soft paste porcelain.
Porcelain	general term for both hard paste (true) and soft paste (artificial) porcelain.
Pottery	potter's ware, clayware. A generic term often used for all fired clayware (ceramics), but more specifically includes only nonvitrified, low-temperature fired earthenware (850°–1100°C). In Europe: Hafnerware.
Rhenish	see: Stoneware.
Rouen	famed soft paste porcelain factory, France.
Salt-glaze	glaze effected by introducing ordinary salt into the kiln at 1050° to 1300°C, where it volatilizes and combines with the surface of stoneware articles to form a glassy sodium silicate.
Semi-porcelain	American whiteware lacking translucency, developed in the 1880s. Also: Semi-vitreous porcelain.
Sèvres	Site of French porcelain factory, famous first for its soft paste, later for its hard paste porcelain.
Slipware	ceramics decorated with slip, a semi-liquid clay mixture. A fine medium for all types of decorations, such as sgraffito, combing and brushing.
Soft paste porcelain	made with glassy substances, i.e., ground glass, mixed with the clay. Fired at about 1100°C. Often finished with low-melting lead glaze. Easily scratched; softer in appearance, but often more pleasing than hard paste. Made by Italians as early as the fifteenth century (Bologna, Medici, Capo-di-Monte), by the French in the seventeenth century (Sèvres, Rouen) and by the Germans and English by the eighteenth century (Meissen, Bow, Chelsea, Derby). Also called "pâte tendre" and "artificial porcelain."
Stoneware	true vitrified pottery, fired in a high-temperature kiln, 1100°–1300°C. Color depends on impurities (metallic oxides) in the clay. Its structure is similar to hard paste porcelain, lacking only its whiteness and translucency. Hard, impermeable. Made in the Rhine valley of Germany as early as the 15th century. Rhenish stoneware (Westerwald, Siegburg, Raeren, Frechen), Kreussen pottery (and its Saxony imitations), 18th- and 19th-century salt-glazed ware all belong to this category. Introduced into America in 1775. German: "Steinzeug"; French: "Grès."

Terra cotta	see: Earthenware.
True porcelain	see: Hard paste porcelain.
Vitrified	chemical transformation of clay, brought about by heat and fusion, causing it to be glass-like: hard, impermeable (and brittle).
Wedgwood	the wares of Josiah Wedgwood: earthenware, stoneware, basalt ware, jasper ware, bone china.
Whiteware	see: Semi-porcelain. Generally any white-bodied ware, white-burning clays, soft paste.

Characteristic: _Type:_	Earthenware	Stoneware	Fine Stoneware	Porcelain
Vitrification:	Nonvitrified	Vitrified	Vitrified	Vitrified
Hardness:	Soft	Hard	Hard	Very Hard
Permeability:	Permeable	Impermeable	Impermeable	Impermeable
Porosity:	10%–15%	Less than 1%	Less than 2%	None
Translucency:	Opaque	Opaque	Opaque	Translucent
Density (weight):	Light	Heavy	Heavy	Heavy
Wall thicknesses:	Thin to medium	Thick	Medium	Medium to thin
Firing temperature ranges:	850°–1000°C	1100°–1300°C	1100°–1250°C	1350°–1500°C
Compositions (typical):				
Clay	80%–90%	30%–70%	30%–70%	40%–70%
Quartz (silica)	10%–20%	30%–60%	30%–60%	25%–40%
Fluxing oxides	(incidental)	5%–25%	5%–25%	15%–40%
Glazes:	Tin, lead	None required (but salt, enamel frits, and slip glazes sometimes used)	None required (but enamel frits and slip glazes are used for decorations)	None required (but porcelain slip glazes often used)
Coloration:	Low-temperature glazes, non-firing enamels, inorganic oxides	High-temperature enamel and glass frits, inorganic oxides	High-temperature enamel and glass frits, inorganic oxides, colored clay slips	High-temperature enamel frits, inorganic oxides dispersed in porcelain slip
First utilized:	In antiquity	12th Cent.	Not known (18th Cent.?)	China: 2nd Cent.(?) Germany: 18th Cent.

MUSTERSCHUTZ AND THE ELUSIVE # MARK

GENE MANUSOV

FOR MANY YEARS WE HAVE BEEN USING THE TERM *MUSTERSCHUTZ* TO DEscribe a certain type of quality porcelain character stein. We use this term almost as we would the name of a manufacturer. The fact that many of these fine pieces were marked with this word on their bases does not give us the right to use this name in conjunction with the stein's maker. Actually, the word *Musterschutz* simply means "copyright," "trademark," or "registered design." Here in the United States we use a patent to protect our designs. In Germany, the words *Musterschutz* or *Gesetzlich Geschützt* were often used to protect the design.

The word *Musterschutz* is not only found on fine porcelain character steins. This label is found on most types of steins, and in many different materials, such as stoneware, salt-glaze stoneware, earthenware, and even pewter pieces. Some character steins made by Albert Jacob Thewalt carry this word incised into the base beside their 1893–1896 trademark. Many relief steins made in stoneware also carry the term on their bases. Many common, ordinary, non-stein–related pieces are labeled *Musterschutz*. Many pieces, especially Munich Child steins, are protected with the magic word. When marked, these porcelain character steins may carry the word *Musterschutz* in green block letters (10a), a blue "#" mark (1a), or both.

It sometimes comes to pass that we adopt incorrect names for certain marks. For some time now we have been referring to the "#" mark as a "hash" mark. Master steinologist, John A. Ey, Jr., recently pointed out this error. The dictionary states that the word *hash* means (in military slang, where the origin of the stein usage was derived) *hashmark*, "a military service stripe worn diagonally or horizontally on the lower sleeve of a uniform, as ///." On the other hand, the word *hatch* means "to mark with parallel crossing lines as ##." Also, *crosshatch* is defined as "a pattern made up of one series of parallel lines."[1] So, *hatch* or *crosshatch* seems more appropriate. We will, from this book forward, refer to this "#" mark as the *crosshatch*, *hatchmark*, or *tic-tac-toe* mark.

Until very recently we have searched in vain attempting to identify the manufacturer responsible for making the steins with the "#" mark. On a recent visit to my home, master steinologist Ron Fox was intrigued by a porcelain character stein of a Sad Monkey (*ECS*-33) that carries the 1b mark of Schierholz and Sohn. This factory is located in the city of Plaue-on-Havel in the Thuringia section of what is now East Germany (DDR). Plaue lies just southwest of Dresden, close to the city of Rudolstadt, home of Ernst Bohne, manufacturer of fine character steins. Being an expert on the materials and decorating methods of the Musterschutz pieces (see "How Musterschutz Steins Were Made"), he detected a definite similarity between my piece (marked *Controll Muster* meaning "sample model") and those bearing the blue crosshatch and/or Musterschutz mark. How ironic if this "missing link" had been sitting on my shelf for over twelve years and I had not known it!

We prevailed upon the Executive Director of Stein Collectors International, Jack Lowenstein, to contact Schierholz (now known as VEB Porzellanmanufactur Plaue) on official SCI stationery to seek further information. We sent them photos of the Sad Radish (*ECS*-25), the Bismarck Radish (*ECS*-264), the L.A.W. Bicycle (*ECS*-459) and the Mushroom (*ECS*-456), along with photos of the base showing the various markings. Much to our delight we received an answer confirming Fox's suspicions. The letter reads, "We are able to tell you that the beer

48

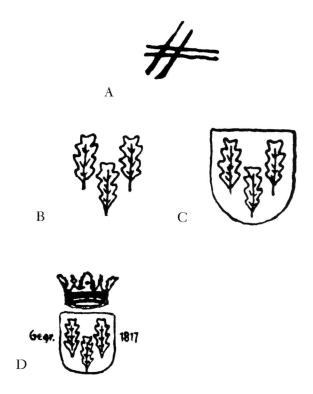

Figure 19. The Schierholz and Sohn trademarks.

steins illustrated on the photographs were produced at our factory at the end of the last century. The models are the work of modellers [designers] Edmund Haase and Edmund Sieder who were employed at our plant during that time."

Their factory was founded in 1817 by Arthur von Schierholz. Upon his death in 1899, the name changed to "von Schierholz'sche Porzellanmanufactur Plaue G.m.b.H." It was at this time that the three oak leaves of the Schierholz coat of arms (Figure 19B) were adopted as a trademark to which a heraldic frame (Figure 19C) was added in 1910.

The first trademark (our elusive "#" mark) dates from the end of the nineteenth century (Figure 19A). It turned out, however, that this symbol had not been registered with the county court at Arnstadt (90 kilometers from Plaue) because only *one* form had been filled out instead of the three prescribed! An attempt was then made to register the mark with the Patent Office in Berlin, but this fell through due to objections raised by the Meissen porcelain factory, who were afraid of confusion with their own trademark.

From about 1930 onward a coronet and the year in which the factory was founded were added to the mark (Figure 19D), sometimes supplemented by "von Schierholz" or "von Schierholz'sche Porzellanmanufactur."

We anticipate that more information will be forthcoming in the near future, but to all *Musterschutz* collectors this is an exciting breakthrough. It will take a long time to call our dear character steins *Schierholz steins*. We will probably always refer to them as *Musterschutz*, just as we continue to call Villeroy and Boch steins *Mettlachs*.

Though we have come a long way in our quest for stein knowledge, we have in fact but scratched the surface. The more we learn, the more we realize how little we really know. It is hoped that books like this will spur others to seek out the truth.

Note:

1. *Webster's New International Dictionary,* 3d ed., s.v. "hash," "hatch," "crosshatch."

49

HOW MUSTERSCHUTZ CHARACTER STEINS WERE MADE

RON FOX

HAVE YOU EVER PICKED UP A BEAUTIFUL MUSTERSCHUTZ CHARACTER STEIN, STUDYING every curve and crevice of its form and carefully examining the smooth, undulating, seam-free inside? You can't help but wonder, "How was this made?" Hopefully, as you read this article it will become apparent what sort of craftsmanship was involved in the production of these porcelain character steins that are marked with the green *Musterschutz* (actually just meaning "copyrighted design") and/or the light blue tic-tac-toe mark.

Mold Making: These Musterschutz characters, judging from their quality, the occasional dates on the pewter rims, and conversations with oldtimers, were made by a factory in the area of Thuringia, Germany, an area famous for its fine porcelain wares. The artists employed by this factory apparently were more or less individually responsible for creating these steins, which not only had to be artistic but also had to be commercially successful. It is safe to speculate that those character steins that are uncommon today were probably not popular when first introduced and were promptly discontinued.

The creative process would begin with the artist sketching his ideas many times until the shape was properly formulated. Next came the modeling, which was done in clay. Of course, in the designing of a stein the artist had to work the handle into the pattern. Other important design considerations were the point at which the separation between the lid and the base would occur, the capacity of the base, and the cleanability of the inside. Only at the point when the artist and his superiors were satisfied with the character's form did the mold-making process begin. The number of parts of each mold and the number of separate molds needed to make the stein depended upon how elaborate the form was. It seems certain that the artists were constrained to as little mold work as possible by their employers who were concerned with production times and the ultimate expense to the buyer.

As a stein repairman I was faced with the task of making an entire lid for the Standing Alligator (*ECS*-430). There were two options available. I could close the mouth of the alligator and use a single mold. Or I could leave the mouth open, and like the original artist I would have to use two separate molds. Since many of these beautiful steins were produced with the more lifelike open mouth and teeth showing, it was decided to follow this same successful path and the two molds were made as can be seen in Figures 20, 21. I was fortunate enough to have gotten another alligator with the top broken exactly where I needed it to be, which enabled me to make the proper molds.

The material used to fill the molds was a fine white porcelain which was considerably more

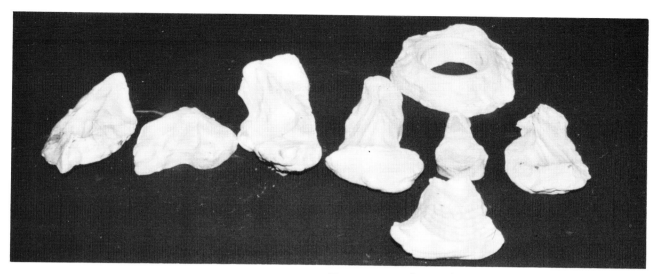

Figure 20. The making of a new lid for the Musterschutz Alligator required two separate molds, shown here in the disassembled state. The three pieces to the left make up the parts forming the upper jaw mold. The five pieces to the right form the balance of the head and the lower jaw of the Alligator.

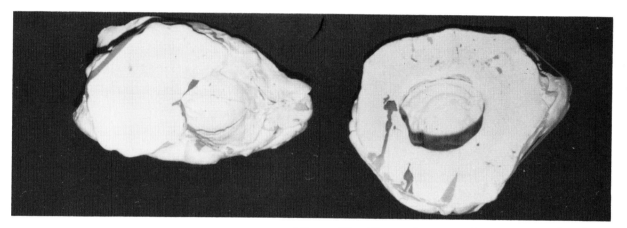

Figure 21. Shown here are the pieces in the above photograph assembled and ready to accept the pouring of the liquid slip.

Figure 22. Ron Fox pouring the slip into the mold.

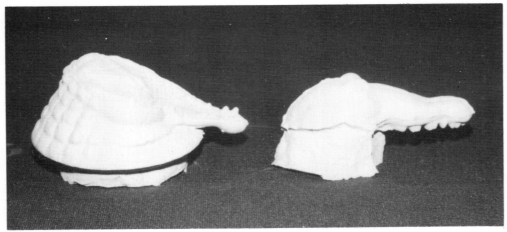

Figure 23. Here are the pieces removed from the mold. The lower jaw is on the left, while the upper jaw and head are on the right.

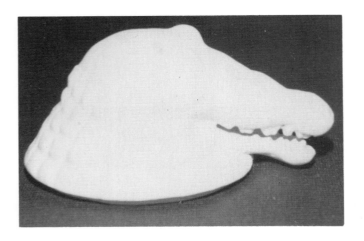

Figure 24. Shown here are the upper and lower parts of the mold joined or "married" together.

Figure 25. At left we see these two sections joined together in the rough stage. In the center we see the same piece after the seams were cleaned and it was fired at 1850°F. The piece to the right is shown after the second firing where white porcelain glaze was added. The piece is now ready to be china-painted.

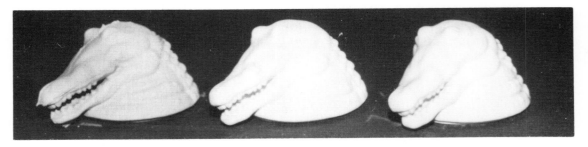

expensive than the stoneware predominantly used for steins. This porcelain clay is made largely of kaolin (a very fine white clay), quartz, and feldspar with all impurities carefully removed. It is translucent, much like milk glass, which made possible the use of lithophanes on certain steins, such as the League of American Wheelmen (*ECS-459*), the Nuremberg Funnel (*ECS-445*), and the Mushroom and Dwarfs (*ECS-456*), among others.

The porcelain used to fill the molds was in a liquid form (see Figure 22). The molds were made of a plaster material which absorbed water from the liquid porcelain "slip," forming a crust on the walls of the mold. After the desired time had elapsed, the unhardened liquid was poured off. The length of time the slip was left in the mold determined the thickness of the piece. After being taken out of the mold (see Figure 23), all of the excess casting had to be cut away so that the two pieces would fit together properly.

At this point, the edges that were to be joined were coated with the liquid porcelain and "*married*" together (see Figure 24). Additional porcelain was applied to the joint to fill any gaps. As these parts were joined together air chambers were created. The artist/technician would have to puncture these chambers, leaving expansion holes such that, in the firing, the heated air could expand so the pieces wouldn't explode, shattering or otherwise ruining many other pieces in the kiln. These holes were normally well hidden within the design. With all the joined porcelain added, the piece was left to air dry for a few days.

At this stage the porcelain would be firm but fragile, and much care had to be taken in its handling. Cutting tools and a damp cloth were used to clean up both the mold seams and joint seams. Any extra detail, such as around the eyes or nose, was now carved. Once the artist was satisfied with the cleaned piece, it was ready for the bisque firing. This traditionally was done in wood- or coal-fired kilns that were less sophisticated than those used now, thus temperature regulation was very difficult. A temperature of about 2200° F was needed to vitrify the porcelain. At the point of vitrification the porcelain would be just at the melting stage, and with slightly higher temperatures the pieces would distort, warp, or melt down altogether. The joined sections, like the jaw of the alligator, were also subject to firing separations, because porcelain shrinks about 20 percent during this first firing, often unevenly, causing joined areas to pull apart. As you can see, of all the clays, porcelain clay is the most difficult with which to work.

Decoration: After the piece cooled from the first firing, a glaze was applied to it, and the piece was refired at 1850°F (see Figure 25). The reason for the lower temperature of the second firing was that the glaze would burn off in the high temperatures required for the first firing. Only a fraction of the pieces made it this far without breaking or developing flaws, and these were then ready for coloring and further firings.

The colorful decorations were accomplished using china paints, sometimes called porcelain enamels, which were then fired at about 1250°F (see Figure 26). The china paint required just the proper use of oil as a medium, or vehicle, and could only be applied by the most skilled decorators at the factory. They used brushes for the fine details and sponges or cheesecloth for the background colors and shadings.

Since the hand painting was individually applied, the full color steins, even of the same

Figure 26. Shown here is the finished product after being painted and fired.

design, could vary greatly in appearance (see Figure 27). The fullest possible palette of colors was available, as can be seen on such steins as the Radish Lady (*ECS-170*) or the Mushroom Ladies (*ECS-159* and 160) (see Figure 28). Thus, the monochromatic decoration of many Musterschutz steins was a constraint of skilled manpower and production time, not a constraint of materials.

The most common monochromatic decoration of the steins involved the use of various shades of beige. Sometimes, however, a stein usually done in beige will be found in a blue and white version. These are generally much lighter in weight, due to an unusually thin porcelain, which, of course, further complicated the handling and firing of these pieces. The blue and white steins, and some others, were decorated with lead glazes rather than the usual china paints.

Figure 27. Three examples of the Gentleman Rabbit (*ECS-62*) showing color variations.

Figure 28. Both Mushroom Ladies (*ECS-159* and 160).

Figure 29. Three different Musterschutz Bismarck
steins (*ECS-132*) showing the blue/white pattern,
full color, and the normal brown/beige tones.

More and more steins found only in the beige tones, or blue and white, are turning up in full color (see Figure 29). It must be that special orders or very limited editions were made, leaving us with endless possibilities of colors and shadings. Collecting these variations can be a joy and an obsession. A few years ago I obtained the Turkish Man (*ECS-161*) in a previously unknown full color version. The search was on, for I felt certain that the similar stein, the Alpine Man (*ECS-165*), must also have been made in full color. It was only recently that I was able to complete this quest (See Figure 30).

Finishing Touches: Like other stein manufacturers of that time, the *Musterschutz* makers were obligated to mark their steins as to their capacities. Unlike the other makers, however, they chose to have the capacity marked on the interior of the stein rather than have it interfere with the outer decoration.

Very few of these Musterschutz steins use the typical device of having a pewter rim attach the lid to the hinge and handle. Most have, instead, the pewter tang that is mounted directly to the porcelain lid via two holes. There are a few reasons for this method. First, it would have been very difficult and expensive to shape a pewter rim to fit the odd lids of most of these steins. Also, due to the concave shapes of the openings, most lids could not be permanently held in place with this rim method. Finally, the artists probably didn't want the pewter to interfere with the lifelike form of the stein.

Though the appearance was greatly enhanced by the omission of the pewter rim, there was a serious problem created. Very often chips, flakes, or fractures occur due to the direct contact between the lid and the base. It is my belief that many of these Musterschutz character steins were seldom bought to serve as functional utensils, but were purchased instead as cherished decorative items. For instance, it is hard to imagine anyone regularly drinking from the Stag Head stein (*ECS-76*) with its very elaborate antlers. These were high quality, luxury items of the time and were respected as such.

Authenticity: Over the years one hears many rumors about forgeries being made of the old character steins. The truth is that they can be made, and with the same quality of years ago, but to do so would be a very expensive operation. In fact, to try and make a forgery of an

Figure 30. The Turkish Man (*ECS*-161) and the Alpine Man (*ECS*-165) in full color versions.

expensive stein sould cost a good deal more than the prices for which the originals are now sold. So collectors can rest easy knowing that their cherished characters are safe from unrecognizable imitations.

Of course, there are cheap reproductions as well as old, high quality, character steins that were not from the *Musterschutz* factory. The easiest way to tell an original Musterschutz is that they usually have the green *Musterschutz* mark and/or the light blue tic-tac-toe mark. Most of them also have small two- or three-digit numbers on the underside of both the lid and the base (see Figure 31). These were quality-control, bench marks, giving credit or blame to the artist who painted the piece. It is unclear why the application of these marks was so inconsistent. It is understandable in cases where a lithophane takes up the entire base of the stein leaving no room for a mark, but not when the entire base is available for marks and none are present. If, however, you learn the telltale signs listed here, you will be able to spot a Musterschutz stein without having to look for a mark.

The following are the most distinguishing features of Musterschutz character steins:

1. Its porcelain is thinner and lighter in weight than others.
2. Its base area is unglazed, giving it a bisque appearance, except where the marks are glazed over.
3. There is always a thin bisque line on the inside and outside of both the top of the base and the bottom of the lid, just where the two meet. It is more noticeable on the inside, which is unpainted.
4. On handling the stein you will feel a very slight roughness to the china paint (although not to the lead glazes).

Because there are Musterschutz steins that carry no marks, other porcelain character steins are sometimes mistaken for Musterschutz pieces, particularly the beige-colored ones. Steins like the Tipsy Cavalier (*ECS*-154), the Sleeping Hunter (*ECS*-164), and the Landlord (*ECS*-195) are often mistaken for unmarked Musterschutz steins. However, when they are closely examined using the above guidelines, it is easy to distinguish them from Musterschutz steins. The porcelain used is of a heavier texture, the base area is highly glazed and scooped out, the telltale bisque lines are missing on the inside of the base and lid, and the

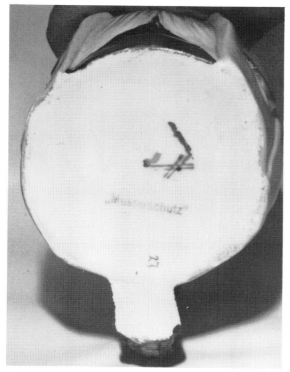

Figure 31. The base of a Musterschutz stein showing all three markings.

Figure 32. The Bismarck copy on the left in full color and the original on the right; note particularly the eyes.

Figure 33. The Musterschutz Drunken Monkey (ECS-39) on the left, and the R.P.M. copy on the right.

overall painting is smoother in texture.

Since World War II many factories have tried to reproduce some of the best of the Musterschutz characters. The two pieces most often copied were the Drunken Monkey (*ECS*-39) and Bismarck (*ECS*-134) (see Figures 32, 33). Other non-Musterschutz steins often copied were the Heidelberg Student (*ECS*-190) and the Hunter Rabbit (*ECS*-64). Some of these copies even carried a black or dark blue tic-tac-toe mark to try to simulate the Musterschutz mark. However, the original tic-tac-toe mark was light blue, and for some unknown reason was always pocked. These copies are altogether cruder than the originals. One of the major reproducers of all four of the above was the Royal Porcelain Manufacturing Company. Their copy of the Drunken Monkey was the best of the four, and if the R.P.M. mark was eliminated, the untrained eye might certainly mistake the copy for a Musterschutz. One identifiable design difference is that the lid on the stein held by the Monkey is wide open on the original, while it is only slightly ajar on the R.P.M. copy (see Figure 33).

I hope this chapter will enable you to better identify, understand, and enjoy the artistry involving in creating the Musterschutz character steins. They are treasures that beautifully represent a legacy of clever porcelain inventions and a heritage of artistic craftmanship.

THE HEXAGRAM AS THE BREWER'S SYMBOL

J. JOSEPH HERSH, M.D.

THE HEXAGRAM IS A SIX-POINTED STAR FORMED BY TWO INTERTWINING TRIANGLES WITH the same center and placed in opposite directions. In Germany the hexagram has been the sign of the brewer and the mark of the tavern for centuries. Its appearance on the gables of ancient taverns was referred to as *Zum guten Stern*, "to the good star." A brewer's tool with a six-pointed star was a *Bierzeiger*, "Beerhand." Early examples of the hexagram in brewing are shown in drawings from Nuremberg, dated 1397 (see Figures 34, 35, 36).

The hexagram is an ancient talisman, a good luck charm, and appeared often in ancient and

Figure 35. Photo found on card with a poem reading: "God does not bless every land with the ability to produce such wonderful beer and wine. They are both very good. Do not forget to thank dear God."

Figure 34. Beer brewing monk, the oldest German representation from a southern work. Drawing from the Mendelschen Brotherhood housebook, Nuremberg 1397.

Figure 36. Ein Bierpreu (A Brewer). Artist: Martin Engelbrecht (1684–1756). Diagram #1—*Bier zeiger* (Beer hand) attached to #5—*Ein Füllkübel* (pail).

Figure 37. Mettlach beaker # 2327/1200 shows the pentagrams over the castle turrets. The State Shield of Hamburg on the beaker's master stein # 2893 has the pentagrams.

medieval magical texts. In the Bronze Age (3500–1100 B.C.) it appeared as a decoration and magical sign in regions as far apart as Mesopotamia and Britain. In the ensuing Iron Age, examples appeared in India and in the Iberian peninsula prior to its Roman conquest.

Considerable literature has accumulated about the hexagram, and this commentary will limit itself to the highlights necessary to solve the mystery of the origin of the hexagram as the sign of the brewer and tavern in Germany. The hexagram is best known as the "Star of David." It was emblazoned upon his battle shield to render him immune to injury. Within the center of the hexagram was the Sixty-seventh Psalm written in the shape of a seven-branched candelabra (David was the author of the Psalms). King Solomon, his son, wore the hexagram as a signet, and it was referred to as the "Seal of Solomon." The ancients considered Solomon as a great magician, rather than a great monarch, due to the miracle of his rapid completion of his celebrated temple at Jerusalem.

During the Middle Ages we find the "Star of David" and the "Seal of Solomon" used in an interchangeable manner and the "Star of David" assuming priority. We also find an erroneous interchange between the hexagram and the pentagram, a five pointed star. The pentagram is the Pentalpha of Pythagoras, a symbol that denotes "Health." Villeroy & Boch shows this error on Mettlach beaker #2327/1200 (see Figure 37). Mettlach #1526 depicts the State Shield of Hamburg with the proper hexagram (see Figures 38, 39).

About A.D. 70 the mystical philosophy of the Jewish religion was described in the treatises of the scholar Simon ben Jochi and called the Kabbala. The Practical Kabbala described the making and use of amulets. The hexagram was involved in two kabbalistic amulets that peaked in the sixteenth century. The doorpost amulet, the mezuzah, is still in use, having its

Figure 38. Mettlach stein # 1526 showing hexagrams over the castle turrets.

Hamburg

Figure 39. The State Shield of Hamburg.

Figure 40. The hexagram on the Ceramic insert of an "Early" Mettlach # 216/1.

Figure 41. Ceramic insert of Mettlach # 2005 shows the hexagram beneath *Wohl bekomm's* (to your health).

Figure 42. The hexagram as a tavern's sign on the body of Mettlach stein # 2028.

Figure 43. The tavern's sign on the body of Mettlach stein # 3090.

Figure 44. The ceramic insert of Mettlach stein # 1997. The bust of the brewer, George Ehret, is on the body of the stein and his initials, G. E., placed in the center of the hexagram.

Figure 45. The Funnel Man. For full description see *ECS*-193.

Figure 46. Close up of hexagram on the Funnel Man.

Figure 47. Sitting Ram (*ECS-70*).

beginning about A.D. 1148. This may have been the beginning of the hexagram placed on homes as a protection against fire.

The "Star of David" became an official Jewish symbol in the fifteenth and sixteenth centuries. The Zionists made it an official symbol at their first congress held at Basel, Switzerland, in 1897.

The *Encyclopedia of Freemasonry* describes the use of the hexagram on the breweries and taverns of Germany in this manner: "Among the old Kabbalistic Hebrews, the Seal of Solomon was, as a talisman of course, deemed to be a sure preventive against the dangers of fire. The common people, seeing this figure affixed always to Jewish brew-houses, mistook it for a sign, and in time in South Germany the Hexagram, or "Seal of Solomon," was adopted by German innkeepers as a sign of a beer-house, just as the chequers have been adopted in England, though with a different history, as the sign of a tavern."

The hexagram has been found on many Villeroy & Boch steins (see Figures 40–44) and also, of course, on character steins (*ECS-70*, 191, 193, 194, 197) (see Figures 45–47).

Were it not for this paragraph from the *Encyclopedia of Freemasonry*, the origin of the hexagram as a brewer's symbol would remain a mystery.

References

Hersh, J. Joseph. "The Hexagram" and "More on the Hexagram." *The Shekel* 14, nos. 2, 3 (1981).

Encyclopedia of Freemasonry. Vol. 1, s.v. "Kabbala." Vol. 2, s.v. "Seal of Solomon" and "Shield of David."

The Universal Jewish Encyclopedia. S.v. "Shield of David."

A LIGHT AT THE END OF THE STEIN—LITHOPHANES

GENE MANUSOV

THE VICTORIAN ERA OF THE EARLY 1800s BROUGHT OUT A GREAT MANY STYLES AND OR-namentations. Some have been termed extravagant and gaudy. Yet, it must be conceded that there were thousands of attractive and choice articles produced in this era that are sought by today's collectors, especially the finer pieces of furniture, figural napkin rings, the choice pieces of glass, and chinaware. In the latter group we can include *lithophanes.*

One of the facets of saving steins or other collectibles is the spin-off of interest in related items. The area which fascinated me most when I was researching the *Encyclopedia of Character Steins* was the beauty of the various lithophanes found on the base of many steins. A review of the literature indicated very little reference material was available. In early 1976 I learned of the upcoming formation of a Lithophane Collectors Club in Toledo, Ohio. Upon becoming a charter member, I had the pleasure of communicating with the founder and curator of the Blair Museum of Lithophanes and Carved Waxes, Mr. Laurel G. Blair.

It is very difficult to describe lithophanes because they are such a different type of art form. To quote Mr. Blair, "Basically it is a porcelain transparency which when held before a light creates a three dimensional image. The image is obtained from the relative thickness of the porcelain. The tones of the thinner areas are lighter, while the thicker the porcelain, the darker the picture. All of the areas are relative, so that the intensity of the light makes no difference, all the various shadings will be relative. The lighting brings out the soft variations of shadings and coloring of the clay."

The traditional process of making lithophanes began by pouring a thin layer of melted beeswax onto a sheet of plate glass, bordered with putty for containment. The artisans worked in front of a light, using fine steel and ivory tools to carve their images in the wax. Where the wax remained the image appeared dark. Where the wax was carved deeply, lighter tones were produced. When unlighted, the wax appeared white and formless.

When the "positive" wax was completed and approved by the manufacturer, a plaster mold "negative" of the image was poured and cured. This mold or "die" was used many times to reproduce subsequent lithophanes. Porcelain slip or paste was then poured into the mold. After drying, the "greenware" was fired at about 2100°F; if color was applied, it was refired at a lower temperature. About twenty to thirty molds could be made from one wax if the carver sharpened the details from time to time. The lithophane was in the "greenware" stage when attached to the body of the stein by the "repairer" in the factory by dipping his finger in water and wetting both surfaces to be joined. Since both pieces were clay they had an affinity for

———— Reprinted by permission of Stein Collectors International from *Prosit* 58 (December 1979): 621–23.

64

each other and would adhere and unite when fired. Lithophanes produced today from old molds are much thicker and coarser than those made in the nineteenth century. This is due to the fact that the workmen are unable to recarve the old wax molds. Because of their inexperience there are many errors and distortions.

Firings took their toll of lithophanes as the wood-fired and gas furnaces were not as carefully controlled as today's modern electronic kilns. The porcelain dough often had impurities which caused many of the lithophanes to crack or be ruined.

Lithophanes are found on hanging panels, panels for lamp shades (including half shades and single casting lamp shades), tea warmers, candle shields, night lights (*veilleuse*), tea cups, tea cup saucers, wall sconces, match boxes, nut dishes, table lamps, table screens, fire screens, ladies fans, and many other items.

The literature shows them called lithopanies, porcelain transparencies, Berlin transparencies, and Berlin night screens.

Though most lithophanes were constructed in Germany, several French and English manufacturers produced them also. Earliest lithophanes are attributed to the King's Porcelain Manufactory *(Königliche Porzellan Manufactur)* which has the mark of "KPM." This pottery, located in Berlin, was purchased by Frederick the Great in 1763 from Johan Ernst Gotzkowsy. The plant was destroyed during World War II, but in recent years has operated from Selb in Bavaria. Other outstanding producers of lithophanes were the Royal Porcelain Company, Minton, Worcester, Meissen, Wedgwood, and Plaue Porcelain Companies, which was known during the nineteenth century as PPM. It is now the von Schierholz Porcelain Manufacturing Company, still making lithophanes today.

Note that the mark of von Schierholz of Plaue, East Germany, used our mysterious "#" or "crosshatch" mark (mark #1a). Mark #1b is still used today by von Schierholz on their lithophanes. See chapter "Musterschutz and the Elusive # Mark."

Though many marks are found on lithophanes (e.g., BPM, EDS & C, EGZ, GMH, HPM, KK, Wedgwood, etc.) to the best of my knowledge none have been found on stein lithophanes, other than the crosshatch which may refer to the manufacturer of the stein.

No lithophane has ever been signed by the artist. It would be difficult for each of the artists to have signed their work as there were so many involved in the making of the finished lithophane.

Talented artists and sculptors were needed to make the master dies from which the lithophanes could be molded. Images reflected copies of the old masters (such as Leonardo da Vinci's "Last Supper"), religious pictures, scenic wonders, and likenesses of presidents, kings, queens, statesmen, and other notables. The genre scenes give an idea of the clothing,

Figure 48. "L.A.W. Bicycle" (*ECS*-458)—cyclists.

Figure 49. "Frauenkirche Tower" (*ECS*-420)— statue of Bavaria.

Figure 50. "Nuremberg Funnel" (*ECS-445*)—the Gooseman Fountain.

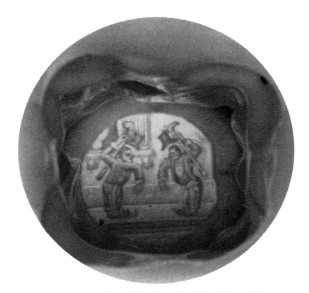

Figure 51. "Umbrella" (*ECS-461*).

furnishings, activities, and thoughts of the people of the nineteenth century. The interest in children, the sentimentality and humor, the outdoor and hunting scenes reveal the life of the times.

The lithophanes range in size from miniatures measuring 1½ inches by 1 inch to plaques as large as 15 inches.

In general, the stein lithophanes often related to the theme of the body of the stein. The "L.A.W. Bicycle" (see Figure 48) depicts cyclists pedaling high wheelers. "King Ludwig II of Bavaria" (ECS-143) shows his famous castle of Neuschwanstein. The "Frauenkirche Tower" (ECS-420) has a beautiful view of the nearby statue of Bavaria in Munich (see Figure 49). Of course, many "Muenchner Kindl" are found with city scenes of Munich. The "Nuremberg Funnel" (ECS-445) has a vivid lithophane of the Gooseman Fountain (*Der Gaensemaechenbrunnen*) found in the plaza of Old Nuremberg (see Figure 50). This stein is often marked with the crosshatch marking. Lithophanes are commonly found on regimental steins depicting military scenes of servicemen leaving or returning from the wars, usually to tearful young frauleins.

Many post–World War II regimental steins have shown images of scantily clad young ladies on the base. They have mostly disappeared in recent production.

Ladies and gentlemen, raise your steins high, drink of the hops and enjoy. But, next time, sneak a peek at the bottom, the light at the end of the stein, after you have quenched your thirst—a surprise may be awaiting you.

FOOTBALL CHARACTER STEINS BY
T. MADDOCKS SONS

MIKE WALD

WHEN WE GAZE AT THE MANY CHARACTER STEINS ON OUR SHELVES, IT BRINGS BACK memories of Germany around the turn of the century. Very few of these treasured character steins were produced here in the United States. Some of the exceptions are the football character steins made by the firm of T. Maddocks Sons of Trenton, New Jersey. Examples of these beauties can be found in figures 96–107 of the *Encyclopedia of Character Steins.*

In researching this stein maker, we learn that in 1869 Thomas Maddock bought the interest of Millington and Paulson and established a pottery known as Astbury and Maddock. At the Centennial Exhibition, they displayed sanitary earthenware and crockery. The firm of T. Maddocks Sons dates from 1893. The original family partners were joined by Moses Collear, C. A. May, and Thomas P. Donoher. The company manufactured fine grades of semiporcelain in table and toilet wares and was well-known for its souvenir line. The firm continued production well into the twentieth century.

The football character steins were first produced in 1905. The patent was issued on 24 January 1905 to Harry S. Maddock, who was presumably one of the sons of Thomas Maddock (see Figure 60). This patent enabled them to exclusively produce steins, mugs, master serving steins, and even tobacco jars, with this design. These were introduced as souvenir items for various United States colleges and universities, including Cornell, Chicago, Columbia, Amherst, Harvard, Princeton, Knox, Northwestern, Yale, University of Pennsylvania, Pittsburgh, as well as many others.

All of their football items carried either a pennant, featuring the school name and colors, or a sports figure. There were at least seven different sports figures featuring:

ECS-99   a standing football player with his hands behind his back.

ECS-100   a football player preparing to pass a football with a *P* on his jersey (usually representing Princeton).

ECS-101   a football player running with the ball and having a *C* on his jersey, representing Columbia.

ECS-102   a baseball pitcher in his wind-up position, with an *H* on his uniform, representing Harvard.

ECS-103   a football player running without the ball, having a *Y* on his jersey, representing Yale.

ECS-104   a football player preparing to drop-kick a football, with a *P* on his jersey from the University of Pennsylvania.

CS-AT-25   rower with a *C* on his shirt representing Cornell.

Figure 53. A ½-liter stein from Yale on the left with a ½-liter mug made into a stein from Cornell on the right.

Figure 52. 2-liter master pouring stein with matching ½-liter, both from the University of Chicago. These were often made as a set consisting of a master stein with either four or six smaller steins or mugs.

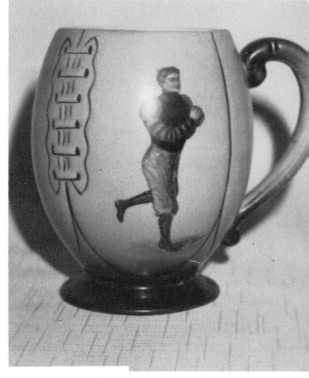

Figure 55. ½-liter mug with the "P" on the jer obliterated so it can be used for special custom ders.

Figure 54. Reverse side of Figure 53, showing the mug having the school seal and the stein without one.

Even though these figures were applied to the pieces via the transfer method, the letters on the jerseys could easily be obliterated and another hand-painted in. Thus, *ECS-103* could be used to represent Michigan by changing the *Y* to an *M*.

All of these figures are hatless and are signed "F. EARL CHRISTY." According to research by Dr. J. Joseph Hersh, Mr. Christy was born in Philadelphia in 1883 and worked as an illustrator in New York in 1934.

All of the drinking steins and mugs were made in the ½-liter size (although no size capacity was ever marked on them). The master pouring stein measures approximately 2 liters in capacity and has a pouring spout. These also were made lidless and thus became pitchers. The colorings on the lidless pitchers resembled the lidless steins or mugs. Very often there were sets made, which included the master pouring stein or pitcher and matching ½-liter mugs or steins (see Figure 52). The tobacco jar produced was slightly larger than the stein (7¾") and its handle was in the form of a lit cigar. In almost all of these cases, the pewter thumblift was in the shape of the head of a football player wearing an old fashioned helmet.

The mugs were the cheapest souvenir items and, consequently, were the biggest sellers. These mugs were very versatile. They all carried either the school pennant or one of the aforementioned figures, or both. In most cases, the mugs also carried the school shield or seal on the reverse side. The handle and base of the mugs, like the pitchers, were always shaded into a darker beige/brown coloring, as opposed to the steins whose handles and bases were a more pronounced black, silver, or gold color. These were solid-colored from the base up the sides of the football seams, rather than evenly shaded like the mugs (see Figures 53, 54). These dark colors on the stein handles and bases often wore off from handling and washing, as is evident in *ECS-99–104*. This is very common among these steins because they were fired at very low temperatures.

Because these steins were made without a pewter rim around the lid, very often chips occurred on the edges of the lid as it would slam closed. This is also very common among these steins.

Maddocks was very innovative. I have come across numerous figure mugs with the letter on the jersey obliterated and a different school pennant or seal applied to the reverse side (see Figures 55, 56). These were usually special orders, and the pennants were probably hand-painted on after the mugs were produced.

Figure 56. Reverse side of Figure 55, showing a hand-painted pennant for an unknown school.

Figure 57. Base of stein showing T. Maddocks markings.

In all cases where the figures are used, we find that they were transferred onto the pieces via the transfer method with the only hand-painting being the letter on the jersey. The school seals were also applied via this process. The pennants, however, were a different story. It seems the pennant outlines were applied while the school names and colors appear to be hand-painted. The two color combinations used most on the pennants were either blue and white or reddish-maroon and white.

The steins, however, did not always carry the school seal. Those with the figures almost always carried the seal as the school's identity was not apparent from the figure alone. Those steins with the school pennant, however rarely carried the seal on the reverse side. I assume it was unnecessary, as the pennant spelled out the school's name. Contrary to the rule about steins, the mugs with pennants almost always carried the school's seal on the reverse side.

Recently, many football character mugs were made into steins by some of the professional stein repairmen. It is easy to spot these, as the base and handle coloring is a tip-off. (See Figures 53 and 54 showing a mug made into a stein on the right and an original stein on the left.)

These pieces were marked at random on the base. When marked, the following appears: "DESIGN PAT. 37297 JAN 24–05 T. MADDOCKS SONS CO. TRENTON, N.J." (see Figure 57).

In an advertisement in the *Cornell Alumni News* dated 20 December 1905 a "Cornell football covered stein" was listed for $2.00. In comparison, in the same advertisement, the Villeroy & Boch ½-liter etched #2872 (the "Cornell" stein) was selling for $2.50, and the 1-liter #2871 etched Cornell was offered at $4.00.

I have seen two mugs not in the shape of a football, but featuring the Yale football figure and the Harvard baseball figure. These also carry the school's seal on the reverse side (see Figures 58, 59). I believe these, too, were produced by T. Maddocks Sons, but I cannot be positive as they are unmarked.

As we have indicated earlier, T. Maddocks made a large variety of souvenir items. Many mugs and pitchers have been found in the conventional shapes honoring various organizations. Those most usually seen are Masonic and Shriners, as well as colleges.

College souvenir mugs are still popular items today, and just about all colleges sell them in their souvenir shops. Perhaps these T. Maddocks steins and mugs were the beginning of a tradition.

Figure 58. Two college mugs showing the same
figures as the character steins.

Figure 59. Reverse side of Figure 58, showing school seals of Yale and Harvard.

UNITED STATES PATENT OFFICE.

HARRY S. MADDOCK, OF TRENTON, NEW JERSEY.

DESIGN FOR A MUG OR STEIN.

SPECIFICATION forming part of Design No. 87,297, dated January 24, 1905.

Application filed December 14, 1904. Serial No. 236,876. Term of patent 7 years.

To all whom it may concern:

Be it known that I, HARRY S. MADDOCK, a citizen of the United States, and a resident of Trenton, in the county of Mercer and State 5 of New Jersey, have invented a new, original, and ornamental Design for Mugs or Steins; and I do hereby declare that the same is fully and clearly illustrated in the accompanying drawing, forming part of this specification.

The drawing illustrates a side view of a 10 mug or stein embodying the design.

What I claim as my invention is—

The ornamental design for a mug or stein herein shown.

HARRY S. MADDOCK.

Witnesses:

WALTER W. ANDERSON,
CHAS. J. BOHLINGER.

Figure 60. Patent issued to Harry S. Maddock in 1905.

MARKS AND MANUFACTURERS

(1a)   (1b)

1. SCHIERHOLZ & SOHN (SON)

    Plaue on Havel (Thuringia), 1817–present.

    The crosshatch, hatchmark or tic-tac-toe mark is one of several used by this company. This firm, located in East Germany (DDR), is now known as VEB Porzellanmanufactur Plaue. (Note: VEB = Volkseigener Betrieb, or People-owned factory.)

2. ERNST BOHNE (later known as "Ernst Bohne Söhne (sons) KG")

    Rudolstadt, Thuringia, 1854–after 1971.
    In 1971 it was known as Albert Stahl and Co.

    (2a)   (2b)   (2c)

3. D.R.G.M. (Deutsches Reichs Gebrauchsmuster).
    Pre-1918.

    D.R.G.M. 154927

    Means design is "registered" or "patented."
    Number 154927, the patent number most commonly found on character steins, was registered to an Adolf Diesinger of Hoehr-Grenzhausen on 9 April 1901.

4. MERKELBACH & WICK

    *Grenzhausen, 1872–1921.
    Started as Merkelbach Stadelmann & Co.

    WICK-WERKE (previously Merkelbach & Wick)
    Hoehr-Grenzhausen, 1921–present.

    (4a)
    1892–1921

    (4b)
    1892–1921

    (4c)
    1921–1937

    Wick Werke **Wick Werke**

    (4d)
    1937–1960

    (4e)
    1960–1972

---

*Hoehr, Grenzau and Grenzhausen later became known as "Hoehr-Grenzhausen."

5. REINHOLD MERKELBACH

*Grenzhausen, Munich, Hoehr-Grenzhausen, 1845–1972.
Sold to Goebel in 1972. Now known as Goebel Merkelbach.

(5a)	(5b)
1882–1933	1911–1916

(5c)	(5d)	(5e)	(5f)	(5g)
1916–1945	1945–1964	1964–1968	1968–1971	1970–1978

6. ECKHARDT & ENGLER KG

*Hoehr, Hoehr-Grenzhausen, 1898–1972.
KG refers to *Kommandit Gesellschaft*, "limited partnership."

(6a)	(6b)

7. ALBERT JACOB THEWALT

*Hoehr, Hoehr-Grenzhausen, 1893–present.

(7a)	(7b)	(7c)	(7d)
1893–1896	1897–1918	1918–1930	1930–present

8. SIMON PETER GERZ G.m.b.H.

*Hoehr, Sessenbach, Hoehr-Grenzhausen, 1862–present.
Staffel, 1977–present (on steins from 1981).
G.m.b.H. means *Gesellschaft mit besohrankter Haftung*," "Company with limited Liabilities."

(8a)	(8b)	(8c)
1862–present	1960–present	1977–present

9. MARZI & REMY

*Hoehr, Hoehr-Grenzhausen, 1879–present.

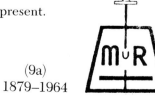  

(9a)	(9b)
1879–1964	1964–present

---

*Hoehr, Grenzau and Grenzhausen later became known as "Hoehr-Grenzhausen."

10. MUSTERSCHUTZ

Means "registered design," "trademark," "patent," "copyright," and "model protection." The cross-hatch mark (1a) is often found in blue on fine porcelain character steins, sometimes in conjunction with the 10a, 10b, or 10c marks.

Musterschutz.

(10a)

„Musterschutz"

(10b)

Musterschutz

(10c)

MUSTERSCHUTZ

(10d)

11. R.P.M. (Royal Porzellan Manufaktur)

Reproduced several character steins during the late 1940s and early 1950s. Made many beautiful porcelain steins in the nineteenth century.

12. JOSEF MAYER, MUENCHEN

There is no evidence that they did any manufacturing or decorating. May have only distributed the steins.

13. JOSEF REINEMANN, MUENCHEN

There is no evidence that they did any manufacturing or decorating. May have only distributed the steins.

(13a)

(13b)

14. MARTIN PAUSON, MUENCHEN

This name was stamped or impressed into stein bases and/or pewter thumblift hinges. Also written on stein bodies (under glaze). There is no evidence, at this time, that they manufactured or decorated any of their steins.

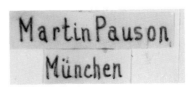

(14a)

(14b)

15. GES. GESCHÜTZT; GESETZLICH GESCHÜTZT and GESCHÜTZT
   Means "protected by law," "patent," and "copyright."

16. VILLEROY & BOCH
   Mettlach, 1836–present.

(16a)
"Mercury" mark since 1874

(16b)
"Castle mark" since 1882

(16c)

17. CAPO-DI-MONTE
   Ginori, Italy, eighteenth century. Widely imitated.

18. REINHOLD HANKE
   *Hoehr, Hoehr-Grenzhausen, 1868–?
   Note: Another person used the (18a) mark, so we cannot assume it is always. Hanke.

RH (18a)

(18b)

(18c) **Reinhold Hanke**

19. DÜMLER & BREIDEN
   *Hoehr, Hoehr-Grenzhausen, 1883–present.
   Stopped stein production in 1957.

(19a)   (19b)

(19c)

20. T.W. (THEODOR WIESELER)
   Nuremberg.
   Distributors. Doubtful if they made any character steins.

(20a)

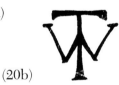

(20b)

21. HR (HAUBER & REUTHER)
   Freising, 1876–approximately 1910.
   There is still some question about these marks belonging to Hauber & Reuther.

(21a)   (21b)   (21c)

22. F&M/N (FELSENSTEIN & MAINZER)
   Nuremberg.
   Pewterers and distributors. They did not make any stoneware stein bodies. They did make some all pewter steins (tankards).

23. STEINZEUGWERKE HÖHR-GRENZHAUSEN G.m.b.H.
   Hoehr, 1912–1925.
   Was an amalgamation of four factories: Reinhold Hanke, Simon Peter Gerz, Reinhold Merkelbach, and Walter Mueller. G.m.b.H. means *Gesellschaft mit beschrankter Haftung,* "Company with limited Liabilities."

---

*Hoehr, Grenzau and Grenzhausen later became known as "Hoehr-Grenzhausen."

24. RASTAL-WERK

Hoehr-Grenzhausen, 1919–present.
Founded in 1919 by Eugen Sahm, father of present-day owners, Werner and Günter Sahm. Originally known as *Sahm-Merkelbach*. Trademark and firm name of Rastal adopted in 1959. Distributor of many contemporary steins. Does not manufacture any character steins, but contracts out to various stein manufacturers and local potterers.

25. MATTHIAS GIRMSCHEID

*Hoehr, Hoehr-Grenzhausen, 1884–present.
Presently known as M. Girmscheid-Wittich. No character stein has ever been seen with any Girmscheid mark; however, character steins are shown in their catalogs. Many of their present-day character steins are distributed by Rastal-Werk and bear their mark (24).

 (25a)  (25b)  (25c)

26. W. GOEBEL PORZELLANFABRIK

Rodental, Bavaria, 1935–present.

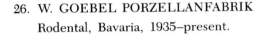

                 (26a)   (26b)
           1950–1955 1960–1963

27. THOMAS MADDOCKS SONS CO.

Trenton, New Jersey, founded 1893.

28. CERAMARTE

Brazil, after World War II–present.
Manufacturers of many character and brewery steins.

29. WERNER CORZELIUS

*Hoehr, Hoehr-Grenzhausen, 1878–present.
Originally known as August Josef Corzelius.

   (29a)   (29b)   (29c)
  1958–1969   1969–?

30. EDELWEISS MARK.

Manufacturer unknown.

---

*Hoehr, Grenzau and Grenzhausen later became known as "Hoehr-Grenzhausen."

31. H. HUTSCHENREUTHER
    Probstzella, Thuringia, 1886–present.

32. GILLES & SOHN (SON)
    *Hoehr, Hoehr-Grenzhausen, 1903–1970s.

 (32a) (32b)

33. HACHIYA BROTHERS COMPANY
    Japan.
    Manufactured or distributed many character steins after
    World war II.

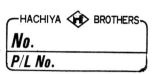 

(33a) (33b)
Paper label affixed
to steins

34. STANGL POTTERY
    Trenton, New Jersey.

35. A. SAELTZER
    Eisenach. Founded 1858.

 (35a)

(35b)

36. DRESDEN ART

37. GEBRÜDER BROTHERS
    Nuremberg.

38. ROSSKOPF & GERZ
    Hoehr, 1901–1917.

39. J. W. REMY (Johann Wilhelm Remy)
    *Hoehr, Hoehr-Grenzhausen, 1864–1966.

(39a)   (39b)   (39c)

*Hoehr, Grenzau and Grenzhausen later became known as "Hoehr-Grenzhausen."

A Germany Glossary
Jack G. Lowenstein

A glossary of German terms and abbreviations found on German antiques, porcelain, pottery, pewter, glassware, and similar items. The list is in alphabetical order, cross-referenced to facilitate finding a given mark, abbreviation, or word.

German			English
A.G.	=	Aktiengesellschaft	Corporation
Ausg.	=	Ausgabe	Edition
Ausgabe			Edition
D.P.a.	=	Deutsche Patentanmeldung	German patent application
D.R.G.M.	=	Deutsches Reichs Gebrauchsmuster	German (State) Patent or protected prototype
D.R.P.	=	Deutsches Reichspatent	German (State) Patent
G.	=	Gesellschaft	Company
Gebr.	=	Gebrüder	Brothers
Gegen Nachbildung Geschützt			Protected (by law) against reproduction, imitation, counterfeiting
Gegr.	=	Gegründet	Established, founded, formed (as a company)
Ges.	=	Gesellschaft	Company
Ges. gesch.	=	Gesetzlich geschützt	Protected by law, patented, copyrighted
Ges. Geschützt	=	Gesetzlich geschützt	Protected by law, patented, copyrighted
Geschützt			Protected (by law)
Gesetzlich Geschützt			Protected by law, patented, copyrighted
G.m.b.H.	=	Gesellschaft mit beschränkter Haftung	Company with limited liability, limited (liability) company, i.e., "Corp." in U.S.A., "Ltd." in England
Made in Germany			Appears on articles made expressly for export after 1892
Musterschutz			Registered patent, copyright, registered pattern
Nr.	=	Nummer	Number
R.P.	=	Reichs Patent	State (Imperial) patent
Salzglasiert			Salt glazed
VEB	=	Volkseigener Betrieb	People-owned factory (East Germany)
Zinn			Tin, pewter

(Note: The German "ü" may be replaced by "ue" in some instances.)

Animals

(Throughout the catalogue asterisks indicate steins made by Schierholz and Sohn.)

AN-1
BERLIN BEAR. ½-liter porcelain; 8″ (20.3 cm). Similar to *ECS*-1, except holding a plain shield. Colored the usual beige/browns associated with the marking of Musterschutz (10).*

AN-2
BERLIN BEARS. ½-liter porcelain. Two variations of the same piece. On the left is the stein previously described, the other is inscribed "*BERLINER GEWERBE AUSSTELLUNG, 1896*" (Berlin Industrial Exhibition, 1896). See *ECS*-1. Marked Musterschutz (10a).*

AN-3
BEAR. ½-liter stoneware; 9″ (22.9 cm). This sedate brown bear holds a beige plaque reading "*Es ist besser mit Katern, Affen u. Bären als allzeit mit Ochsen u. Eseln zu verkehren.*" (Your precious time is better spent with tom-cat, ape and bear. The stubborn ox and foolish ass let other folks repent.) The tail forms the handle. No marks, only mold-mark # 1455. Possibly Steinzeugwerke (23).

79

*Made by Schierholz and Sohn.

AN-4

BERLIN BEAR. ½-liter porcelain; 7″ (17.8 cm). Similar to *ECS-71*, except in a delicate blue/white coloring. This piece was identified as a "Wolf" in *ECS*. Close examination shows the snout being much too short for a wolf, the ears too are much more bear-like than wolf-like. The bear, of course, is the symbol of the city of Berlin. Certain regiments had the bear as their motif, if not their actual mascot. Dancing bears were very popular at German carnivals in the 17th, 18th, and 19th centuries. The spiked helmet would tend to confirm its army connection (credit to Arthur Maethner). Marked Musterschutz (10a).*

AN-5

BERLIN BEAR. ½-liter porcelain; 5¾″ (14.6 cm). This stylized barrel has a very ornate handle in the shape of the Berlin Bear (*ECS-1*). The Shield of Berlin lies on the lid. Colored in the usual beige/browns associated with the Musterschutz (10a) marks. A gold number 29 is lettered on the bottom.*

AN-6

BOARS. ½-liter porcelain; 7¼″ (18.4 cm). Group photo of *ECS-3* and 4. The boar on the left is a greyish beige, the other greyish green. Marked Musterschutz (10a) and the Crosshatch Mark (10e).*

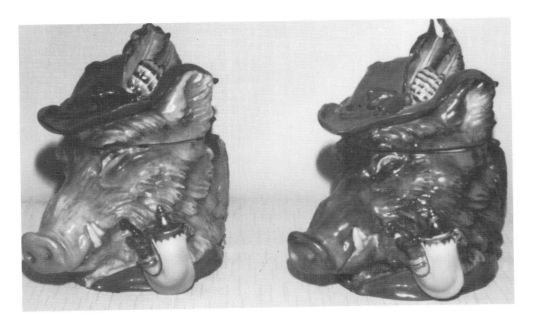

*Made by Schierholz and Sohn.

AN-7

BULL. ½-liter stoneware; 7¾″ (19.7 cm). Sitting on his haunches, this grim brown animal (symbolic of a stubborn blockhead), is wishing the drinker "Prosit." No marks, only moldmark #1453. Identified as Steinzeugwerke (23). See "Old Catalogs."

AN-8

BLACK CAT WITH HANGOVER. ½-liter porcelain; 7½″ (19 cm). Similar to *ECS-5*, except for the grey/black coloring. The word "Hidegeigey" is lettered on his white chest. "Hidegeigey" (sometimes spelled Hid*i*geigey), the black tomcat, is a famous character from Joseph Viktor von Scheffel's "The Trumpeter of Saeckingen" (Der Trompeter von Saeckingen). In the poem Hidegeigey is the companion to the heroic trumpeter, Werner. He serves as Scheffel's vehicle of humor and wit, a feline philosopher. According to Proelss, a friend of Scheffel, there really was a Hidegeigey. The original cat was extremely intelligent and was the pet of a Prussian judge named Preuschen. The cat is also found on the #2007 Mettlach stein. Marked Musterschutz (10a) and the Crosshatch (10e).*

AN-9

CAT WITH HANGOVER ON PEDESTAL. ½-liter porcelain; 9½″ (24.1 cm). A rare variation of the feline. The 1½″ recessed base allows the placement of a music box. Marked Musterschutz (10a).*

*Made by Schierholz and Sohn.

AN-10

BLACK CAT. ½-liter stoneware; 8″ (20.3 cm). This feline holds several light beige fishes under both paws. She is also grasping a beige bottle (inscribed *"antibrin"*) under her right paw. The large scroll reads: *"Der Kater ist ein Leid fuerwahr Vor dem es jedem schaudert. Ein Mittel gibt's degegen zwar Doch wird's nicht ausgeplaudert. Denn ist das Mittel erst bekannt, Denn nimmt das Saufen ueberhand Es sauft her noch Alt oder Jung Und uns trifft die Verantwortung."* (The hangover is a painful sorrow, which many suffer when it be the morrow. Yet though there's a cure, we can't be sure, if its secret we should borrow. Were the formula told, then guzzlers, young and old, would nevermore their liquor hold, and we would bear the shame, the blame.) Marked Merkelbach & Wick (4a).

AN-11

BLACK CAT. ½-liter stoneware; 8″ (20.3 cm). Similar to the previously described Black Cat. This scroll reads: *"Hast du Kater, ist mein Rath: Trinke früh, was du trankst spat."* (My advice to those hungover: Drink by the dawn's new light, the beverage you consumed last night.) Marked Merkelbach & Wick (4a).

AN-12

CAT WITH MANDOLIN. ½-liter stoneware; 10″ (25.4 cm). Similar to *ECS-16*, however, in this variation our little feline holds a musical instrument instead of the seltzer bottle. The mandolin rests on an inverted beige "HB" mug. Colors are greys and blacks, with a blue bowtie. The inscription reads:

"Lass deinem Durste freien Lauf- Bei mir kommt kein Kater auf." (Let your thirst run free, another hangover you'll never see.) Marked Reinhold Merkelbach (5a), #662 GESCHÜTZT.

AN-13

KITTEN WITH BABY. ¼-liter stoneware, 6″ (15.2 cm). Third member of the "family" shown in *ECS-12*. The baby kitten lies comfortably on a grey blanket. The light tan handle is embossed with flowers and vines. Single jeweled base. Marked D.R.G.M. 154927 (3), GESETZLICH GESCHÜTZT. Moldmark #737.

AN-14

KITTEN WITH YARN. ½-liter stoneware; 6¾″ (17.1 cm). Same as the middle-sized cat shown in *ECS-12*. Colors are various shades of yellows, browns, and beiges. Double-jeweled base. Marked D.R.G.M. 154927 (3), moldmark #701 B.

AN-15

CAT. ½-liter porcelain; 7″ (17.8 cm). The brown body is painted to simulate a barrel. The grey and black head of a cat peers out of the lid. A colored lithophane on the bottom shows a monk placing a chain around a young girl's neck. No marks.

83

AN-16
CAT. ¼-liter stoneware; 5¾″ (14.6 cm). A smaller version of *ECS*-11. Marked Simon Peter Gerz (8a), GES. GESCH. GERMANY, moldmark #062.

AN-17
CAT. ¹⁄₁₆-liter stoneware; 4″ (10.2 cm). Here we see *ECS*-11 (right) with her "mirror-image" sister. Notice the similarities in the two pieces, except for the different position of the cap on her head. Marked Simon Peter Gerz (8a) and 030 GERMANY.

AN-18
RICH CAT. ½-liter stoneware; 7¼″ (18.4 cm). This nattily attired feline resembles several of the rich man steins seen throughout both character books. Colored beige, brown, and green. No marks, only the moldmark #511.

AN-19

BICYCLE WITH CAT. ½-liter porcelain; 7″ (17.8 cm). The base of this stein is similar to *ECS-458*, however, the usual shielded lid is replaced by a porcelain Kater, his right paw holding his aching head. The large lithophane once again shows a scene of a young man falling off his bike onto a woman. Marked Musterschutz (10a).*

The members of bicycle clubs often stopped at taverns for a nip along the way. They occasionally wound up in a state of inebriation. Hence, the drunken cat finial.
(Information by bicycle collector, Louis Schultz)

AN-20, 21

DACHSHUND. ½-liter stoneware; 10½″ (26.7 cm). This pitiful, begging canine appears in a lifelike brownish coloring. A similar light version is seen on the left. No marks, only the moldmark #1448. Possibly Steinzeugwerke (23).

AN-20

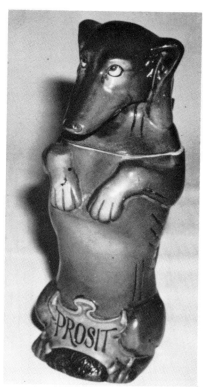

AN-21

AN-22

POODLE. ½-liter stoneware; 9″ (22.9 cm). This light beige poodle, a blue scarf wrapped around its neck, is clutching a black or brown bowling ball in its paws. No marks, only moldmark #1452 is incised in the bottom.

*Made by Schierholz and Sohn.

AN-23
SHAGGY DOG. ½-liter stoneware; 8″ (20.3 cm). A blue/grey variation of *ECS-19*. No marks, identified as Simon Peter Gerz (8a).

AN-24
SITTING DOG. ½-liter stoneware; 8″ (20.3 cm). An older version of *ECS-18*. Details of this piece are finer. The overall coloration is a light brown. No marks, only the incised moldmark #101 GERMANY. Identified as M. Girmscheid (25).

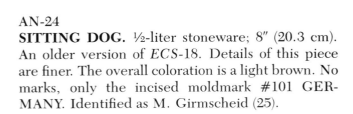

AN-25
BULLDOG. ¼-liter stoneware; 6½″ (16.5 cm). Similar to the Bulldog, *ECS-22*. This brown piece wears a red bowtie, a flower appears on the beige panel between his paws. No marks, only the incised moldmark #1440. This stein was also made in a ½-l. size with German verse in the panel (instead of flower).

AN-26

DONKEY. ½-liter stoneware; 9½" (24.1 cm). Wearing a tan coat, white shirt, and burnt-orange tie, this bluish-grey *Esel* (Ass) is ready to "do the town." According to Roland Henschen, the German word *Esel* can also stand for a fool or buffoon. Possibly this is what this stein is intended to portray. Sometimes associated with a person who could not hold his liquor very well (ca. late 19th century). No marks, only the moldmark #1454. Identified as Steinzeugwerke (23). See "Old Catalogs."

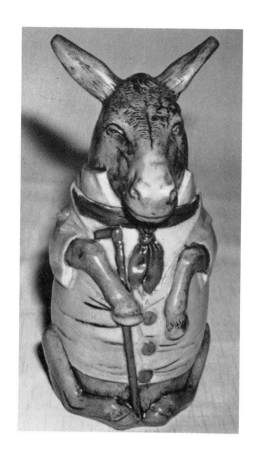

AN-27, 28, 29

TEDDY ROOSEVELT. ½-liter stoneware; 12" (30.5 cm). A rare elephant stein with Teddy sitting atop its head. Roosevelt, of course, was a noted elephant hunter in his day. No marks, only GERMANY.

AN-29

AN-27

AN-28

87

AN-30
FOX. ¼-liter stoneware; 6″ (15.2 cm). The smaller variation of the master stein *ECS-31*. The body consists of varying shades of beiges, browns, and yellows. The Bavarian pipe has a red cord entwined around it—the same color as his small cap. In his left paw is a pilsner of foaming beer. The handle is embossed with vines and flowers. Marked D.R.G.M. 154927 (3), moldmark #739, GERMANY, GESETZLICH GESCHÜTZT.

AN-31
GENTLEMAN FOX. ½-liter stoneware; 7½″ (19 cm). Similar to *ECS-28*, except in full, bright enamelled colors. The stein actually represents a first year fraternity member *(Fuchs)*. Note the cap and fraternity colors. No marks, only the incised #54. A black-letter HR,32 appears on the bottom of some pieces. They may represent the decorator who painted this stein. See Jester, Monk, and Nun for others in this series.

AN-32
GENTLEMAN FOX. ½-liter stoneware; 6¼″ (15.9 cm). A nattily attired blue/grey salt-glazed "rich" fox. No marks. Identified as Reinhold Hanke (18), moldmark #458. See "Old Catalogs."

AN-33

HUNTER FOX. ½-liter stoneware; 7¾″ (19.7 cm). Our happy foxes appear to be dressed for a little hunting. As is common with many of the animal steins, the hunted are the hunters. The brown sacks are supported by black straps. No marks, only moldmark #1441. Steinzeugwerke (23). See "Old Catalogs."

AN-34

LION. ½-liter porcelain; 7″ (17.8 cm). This mustached, monacled animal could be a comical caricature of the British lion. Colorings are the usual beige/browns of Musterschutz (10a).*

AN-35

SITTING LION. ½-liter porcelain; 7″ (17.8 cm). Beautiful full-figured lion, has its tail form the handle. Beiges and creams. Marked Musterschutz (10a) and Made in Germany.*

*Made by Schierholz and Sohn.

AN-36
BAVARIAN LION. ½-liter stoneware; 7½″ (19 cm).
This full-figured lion wears a beige/brown crown.
The blue and brown shield of Bavaria is draped
across the front. Marked Reinhold Merkelbach
(5a), moldmark #20.

AN-37
MONKEY. ½-liter stoneware; 8¾″ (22.2 cm). This
bluish/grey salt-glazed figural has the "mutton-
chops" so reminiscent of Kaiser Wilhelm I (see
ECS-148,149). The verse reads: *"Der Kater laut
Erfahrung stirbt am sauren Harung."* (A sour her-
ring for those past caring is bound to help them
restore their bearing.) No marks.

AN-38
MONKEY. ½-liter stoneware; 10″ (25.4 cm). This
sitting monkey holds a very large boot between his
paws. The German word for boot is *Stiefel* which
also means a large tankard. The symbolism is self-
evident. His large tail wraps around to form the
handle. The lid is formed in the shape of a green
and black jockey's cap. No marks. Identified as
Reinhold Hanke (18) #1088. See "Old Catalogs."

AN-39

ORANGUTAN. ½-liter porcelain; 6″ (15.2 cm). This bisque head of an anthropoid ape has the quality of workmanship associated with the anchor mark of Ernst Bohne (2a).

AN-40

SITTING MONKEY. ½-liter stoneware; 7¼″ (18.4 cm). This "hobo" is attired in a tattered red coat and black top hat. He opens a beige stein. A yellow flower is tucked in his lapel. No marks, only moldmark #1442.

AN-41

MONKEY WITH PIPE. ½-liter stoneware; 9¼″ (23.5 cm). Similar to the previous stein, this German symbol of intoxication also wears a blue coat with both sleeves torn. An incised plaque on the rear reads: *"Wird der Aff im Bierfass gross, ist auch gleich der Teifel los."* (When the ape grows huge in its cask of beer, the forces of hell will bring you no cheer.) The base inscription reads: *"Trag Deinem Affen mit Geduld An dem bist du nur selber Schuld."* (Carry your ape with patience and shame. You have no one but yourself to blame). No marks, only moldmark #828, GERMANY.

AN-42

SITTING MONKEY. ½-liter stoneware; 7½″ (19.1 cm). Similar to *ECS*-44. This fancy dude sports a small pair of binoculars in his right front paw, a pipe in his left, and a foaming mug of brew in his right hind paw. Perched on his snubby nose is a tiny pair of granny glasses. A tan hat sits atop his brown head. Single-jeweled base. Marked D.R.G.M. 154927 (3), GESETZLICH GESCHÜTZT, Mold-mark #817.

AN-43

SITTING MONKEY. ½-liter stoneware; 9¼″ (23.5 cm). A mate to the prior stein and *ECS*-44. He sports a brownish cone-shaped hat. A red necktie dangles from his collar, through the pewter rim. A pink rose is tucked in his gold vest. In his left paw is a grey letter. The end of the handle depicts the face of a snake. Marked D.R.G.M. 154927 (3), mold-mark #858, GES. GESCHÜTZT, GERMANY.

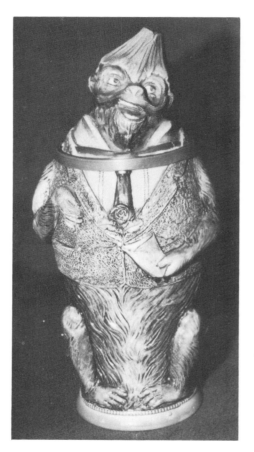

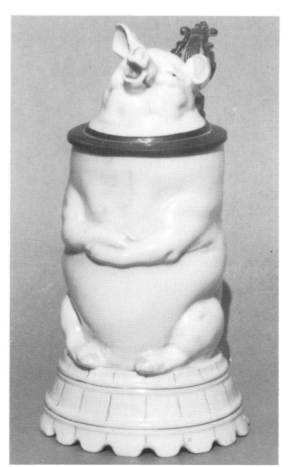

AN-44

SINGING PIG STANDING ON BARREL. ½-liter porcelain; 9¼″ (23.5 cm). Similar to *ECS*-57, however, this variation has folded arms as seen in *ECS*-56. The 2″ recessed base has provisions (three indentations) for a music box. Marked Musterschutz (10a).*

*Made by Schierholz and Sohn.

AN-45
PIG SMOKING PIPE STANDING ON BARREL.
½-liter porcelain; 8¼″ (21 cm). Similar to *ECS-49*. The lifelike colors consist of white and pink. Music box base which looks like a circus stand (or barrel) is yellow with brown bands. Musterschutz (10a). The Pig is a sign of good luck.*

AN-46
PIG. ½-liter stoneware; 7″ (17.8 cm). This rich little piggy is so loaded that he can afford to let his money leak out of his sack. He must feel lucky, as there is a green four leaf clover dangling from his mouth. Beige body, pink money bag, jeweled base. Marked D.R.G.M. 154927 (3), moldmark #689, GERMANY.

AN-47
SEATED GOAT ON PEDESTAL. ½-liter porcelain; 9½″ (24.1 cm). Similar to Seated Ram, *ECS-65*. Note the change from ram to goat. The word ram, by definition, is a male sheep (characterized by the ram's horns and the *absence* of any beard). Both *ECS-65* and this stein *have* beards, hence they are not rams, but billy goats. The barrel-like pedestal base can support a music box. Same coloration as *ECS-65*. Marked Musterschutz (10a).*

*Made by Schierholz and Sohn.

GOAT. ½-liter porcelain; 6″ (15.2 cm). A beige/brown variation of the blue/white piece shown in *ECS*-66. This *Bock* is seen more often than the rarer onion-patterned stein. Marked Musterschutz (10a).*

AN-49
GOAT. 3-liter stoneware; 14½″ (36.8 cm). This very large pouring stein is incised with the saying: "*Es stiess der Bock den Braven. Kommt last ihn, er mag schlafen.*" (Even the strongest ones must cower, before that stalwart bock-beer power.) Marked D.R.G.M. 154927 (3), GESETZLICH GESCHÜTZT, GERMANY.

AN-50
BILLY GOAT. ¼-liter stoneware; 5½″ (14●cm). Another variety of barrel stein. Here the goat's head pops out of the pewter-rimmed lid. For other examples, please see *ECS*-68, 69. The front panel says: "*Lieb Dich für Schaum ist kein Bier.*" (Though foam be not beer, True love remains dear.) Marked D.R.G.M. 154927 (3), moldmark #722, GESETZLICH GESCHÜTZT.

*Made by Schierholz and Sohn.

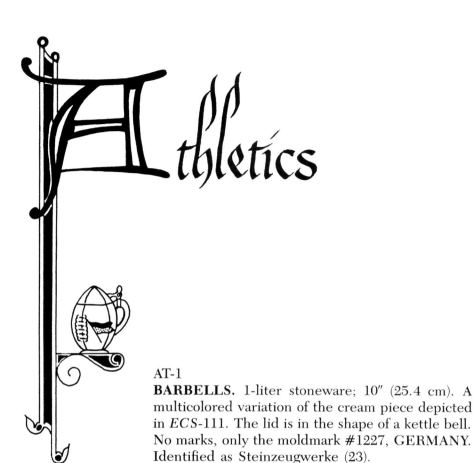

Athletics

AT-1
BARBELLS. 1-liter stoneware; 10″ (25.4 cm). A multicolored variation of the cream piece depicted in *ECS*-111. The lid is in the shape of a kettle bell. No marks, only the moldmark #1227, GERMANY. Identified as Steinzeugwerke (23).

AT-2
BARBELLS. The cream/dark green style alongside the grey/green. No marks, moldmark #1227, GERMANY. *Both* identified as Steinzeugwerke (23).

AT-3
BOWLING PINS. ½-liter porcelain. Three variations of *ECS*-80. Blue/white, wood-grain brown, and cream (seen either with or without a lithophane). All marked Musterschutz (10a).*

AT-4
BOWLING BALLS. ½-liter porcelain; 4½″ (11.4 cm). Similar to *ECS*-78, but with two different colorations. On the left, a light beige; the other, a glazed brown wood-grain pattern. Matching porcelain thumblifts. Marked Musterschutz (10a).*

AT-5
BOWLING PIN. ½-liter porcelain; 8¾″ (22.2 cm). Similar to *ECS*-79, however, in this piece the coloring is a glossy white. The raised figures are polychromatic. A lithophane shows a similar scene to the front. Marked Musterschutz (10a).*

*Made by Schierholz and Sohn.

AT-6
BOWLING PIN. ½-liter porcelain; 8¾″ (22.2 cm). Similar to the previous stein, but here the colors are the rare blue/white patterns. Blue flowers are scattered throughout the base and lid. Blue handle. Marked Musterschutz (10a).*

Kegling was originally played with Nine pins and often called "Nine Pins!" Layed out like this:

This game was forbidden to the common people, especially on Sunday, so they added another pin, called it "Ten pins," and played it anyway!!

AT-7
BOWLING PIN. ½-liter porcelain; 9¼″ (23.5 cm). This wood-grained piece shows a relief pin-boy jumping atop three shields. The black silhouette of a dog appears on the left shield, a red cow on the right, the center has a large "9" found on many kegling steins. A red, white, and black banner hangs below. The pewter lid rim is dated 1895. No Marks.

AT-8
BOWLING PIN. ³⁄₁₀-liter porcelain; 5½″ (14 cm). Resembling *ECS*-90, but in a brownish wood-grain finish. Marked Musterschutz (10a) with the cross-hatch (1a).*

*Made by Schierholz and Sohn.

AT-9
BOWLING PIN. ½-liter stoneware; 8″ (20.3 cm). Similar to *ECS*-84 and 85. This stein is a monochromatic cream color. No marks, only mold-mark # 1134, GERMANY. Identified as Steinzeug-werke (23).

AT-10
BOWLING PIN. ½-liter stoneware; 10½″ (26.7 cm). Similar to *ECS*-80, except the body color is a cream wood-grain. No marks, only mold # 1140. Identified as Steinzeugwerke (23).

AT-11
BOWLING PINS. Two versions of *ECS*-80, the brown wood-grain on the left, cream on the right. Steinzeugwerke (23).

AT-12
BOWLING PIN. 1½-liter stoneware; 15″ (38.1 cm). Similar to *ECS*-81, except for the cream coloring. The pinsetter is sitting atop a large "9" instead of a sling. No marks, only moldmark #1186. GERMANY. Identified as Steinzeugwerke (23).

AT-13
BOWLING PIN. 1½-liter stoneware; 15¼″ (38.7 cm). Similar to the previous stein. Once again the pinsetter sits on the large gold "9." The wood-grain coloration is a deeper brown. Another version shows the relief highlights in full color. No marks. Identified as Steinzeugwerke (23), #1186. See "Old Catalogs."

AT-14
BOWLING PINS. 1½-liter stoneware; 15″ (38.1 cm). Two variations of moldmark #1186. *ECS*-81 on the right.

AT-15

BOWLING. ½-liter stoneware; 9″ (22.9 cm). Similar to *ECS*-95, except the lid/body separation is located in the neck of the nine bowling pins—this creates a less cumbersome lid. The coloring of the base legend is cream on a green background. It reads: *"Kegelspiel u. Bier, Ist mein Pläsier."* (Bowling and beer provide my cheer.) No marks. Possibly Steinzeugwerke (23).

AT-16

BOWLING BALL. ½-liter porcelain; 5½″ (14 cm). Greyish-white in coloring. Beige pins are scattered. *"Gut Holz"* (Good wood) across the front. Similar to *ECS*-77. Marked H. Hutschenreuther (31).

AT-17

BOWLING. 1-liter stoneware; 12″ (30.5 cm); ½-liter 9″ (22.9 cm). A larger bowling pin shown with *ECS*-95, on the right. The same inscriptions read: *"Lustig is die Kegelei, Leib und Seele macht sie frei."* (The sport of bowling must ever be, Are body and soul both to be free.) Literally, the idea is that the sport of bowling frees body and soul and that bowling is fun. No marks, only moldmark #1222 GERMANY. Possibly Steinzeugwerke (23).

AT-18

FOOTBALL. 2-liter porcelain; 12″ (30.5 cm). Master pouring stein depicting the blue pennant of Northwestern University. Marked T. MADDOCKS SONS CO (27).

AT-19

FOOTBALL. 2-liter porcelain; 12″ (30.5 cm). Similar likeness to *ECS-98*, however, here we see the red and white pennant of the University of Chicago. The pewter thumblift is topped with the helmeted head of an old-time football player. Marked T. MADDOCKS SONS CO. (27).

AT-20

FOOTBALL. 2-liter porcelain; 12″ (30.5 cm). Another large master stein, similar to *ECS-98*. A decal of a Princeton football player appears on one side, the school seal on the other. Also made as a ½-liter, lidless mug. Marked T. MADDOCKS SONS CO. (27).

AT-21
FOOTBALL. 2-liter porcelain. Matching ½-liter drinking stein.

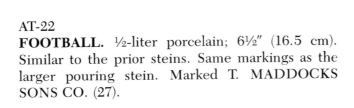

AT-22
FOOTBALL. ½-liter porcelain; 6½″ (16.5 cm). Similar to the prior steins. Same markings as the larger pouring stein. Marked T. MADDOCKS SONS CO. (27).

AT-23
FOOTBALL. ½-liter porcelain; 6½″ (16.5 cm). Similar to *ECS*-106, except with the black and orange pennant of Princeton. Marked T. MAD DOCKS SONS CO. (27).

AT-24
FOOTBALL. ½-liter porcelain; 6½″ (16.5 cm). Similar to the prior, but with the blue and yellow flag of Michigan. Overall coloring is a deeper pigskin "tan" to highlight the yellows of the pennant. Marked T. MADDOCKS SONS CO. (27).

AT-25
FOOTBALL. ½-liter porcelain; 6½″ (16.5 cm). Another matched drinking vessel to *ECS* 101–104. The athlete carrying the oar has the red "C" of Cornell on his blouse. The school seal of Cornell appears on the reverse side. Also produced as a 2-liter master pouring pitcher and as a ½-liter mug. Marked T. MADDOCKS SONS CO. (27).

ECS 100–104 feature various sport figures. The photos on this page show the reverse side, depicting the school seals.

AT-26
CORNELL. Reverse of prior stein.

AT-27
PRINCETON. Reverse of *ECS-100*.

AT-28
COLUMBIA. Reverse of *ECS-101*.

AT-29
HARVARD. Reverse of *ECS-102*.

AT-30
YALE. Reverse of *ECS*-103.

AT-31
PENNSYLVANIA. Reverse of *ECS*-104.

AT-32
FOOTBALL. ½-liter stoneware; 6¼″ (15.9 cm). This tan pigskin has the lifelike incised laces on the side. The "P" pennant may depict the gold and black colors of Purdue. No marks, only GER-MANY.

AT-33
FOOTBALL. ½-liter stoneware; 6¼″ (15.9 cm). This stein shows four pennants along the side. The orange and black coloring on the upper two indicate the possibility they might be Princeton. The pennants on the body are the gold and black of Purdue. No marks, only GERMANY.

AT-34
SOCCER BALL. ½-liter stoneware; 5″ (12.7 cm). In Germany, the game is not called soccer, but is known as *Fussball* or *Fussballspiel*, which, of course, translates to "Football." Similar to *ECS-115*, except for the cream coloring. No marks. Identified as Steinzeugwerke (23).

AT-35
SOCCER BALL. ½-liter stoneware, 6″ (15.2 cm). This ball is very similar to the modern-day brown leather soccer ball. Three small legs support the pedestal base. This piece is also found in a cream color. No marks. Identified as Steinzeugwerke (23).

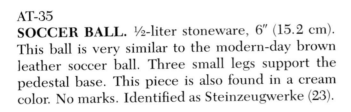

Owls—Universal symbols of wisdom

Myths and superstitions surround the venerable bird of the night. Its eerie, spine-chilling night call has given it a reputation as a creature of ill-omen, forecasting doom and death. The Chinese call the owl "the bird which snatched away souls." An ancient Greek superstition says that eating its eggs prevents drunkenness (possibly why there are so many owl steins), although the owl also had a more respectable role in classical Athens where it was the symbol of wisdom. For more information on the symbolism of the owl please refer to the "Owls on Steins" by Arthur Maethner (*Prosit*, no. 33, page 197, December 1973). Also "Wise Old Steins," by Liselotte Lopez (*American Collector*, June 1976).

Another interesting connection with the owl has been expounded by Roland Henschen. The connection is with the potter or pottery maker himself. The German word for owl is *eule: die eule; der uhu*—old words for pottery makers were *eulner* or *euler*, because they stayed up all night (like the owl) to tend their ovens. Another thought on this—the German sounds for *eu*, *u* and *au*, and the fact that old writing did not always have the spelling well established, an old word for pottery oven was *ullen*, which came from the word *ulla*—an old word for pot. All this language derived from the idea that clay pots were made by potters who stayed up like owls to tend their ovens at night. In the Middle Ages there was a pottery street in Siegburg called *Aulgasse* which translated to "pottery street" or "street of the potters."

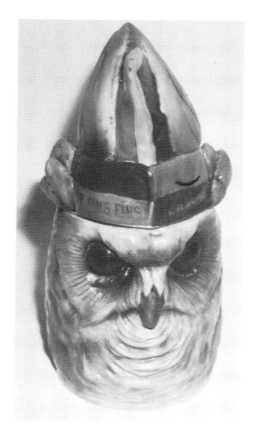

BD-1
INDIAN CHIEF OWL. ½-liter porcelain; 9″ (22.9 cm). A fine, wise companion to the OWL WITH JESTER'S CAP, *ECS*-120. This brownish-gray nocturnal bird is wearing a red, blue, yellow, and beige headdress. Inscribed along the band is "*R. EINS EINS S/L JÖRG.*" The inscription refers to the fact that the owl was given to *Ritter Eins Eins by Ritter Joerg*, both of whom were "knights" in a German fraternal society known as "Schlaraffia." The handle consists of an owl's foot with talons. Glass eyes are cemented to the vessel. Marked Musterschutz (10a).*
(Credit to our poet laureate, Art Maethner, the only member of SCI who is also a member of Schlaraffia)

*Made by Schierholz and Sohn.

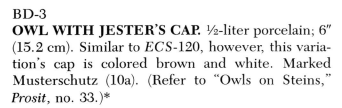

BD-2

OWL. ³⁄₁₀-liter porcelain; 4½″ (11.4 cm). Similar to *ECS*-121, this beautiful bisque bird's brows narrow down to the pointed beak. Brown and yellow plumage. No marks. Possibly Ernst Bohne (2).

BD-3

OWL WITH JESTER'S CAP. ½-liter porcelain; 6″ (15.2 cm). Similar to *ECS*-120, however, this variation's cap is colored brown and white. Marked Musterschutz (10a). (Refer to "Owls on Steins," *Prosit*, no. 33.)*

BD-4

OWL. 1-liter stoneware; 14½″ (36.8 cm). This bird of the night perches on a beige base. The lid, which forms the head is a chocolate color. No marks, only the number 83/M appears on the bottom. Identified as Steinzeugwerke (23), # 1662. See "Old Catalogs."

*Made by Schierholz and Sohn.

BD-5
WHITE OWL. ½-liter porcelain; 7½″ (19.1 cm). This stately bird appears to have a slight twinkle to his tiny black eyes. Anyone for a cigar? No marks. Ernst Bohne (2).

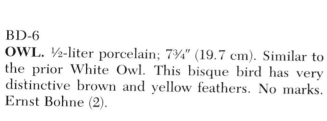

BD-6
OWL. ½-liter porcelain; 7¾″ (19.7 cm). Similar to the prior White Owl. This bisque bird has very distinctive brown and yellow feathers. No marks. Ernst Bohne (2).

BD-7
EAGLE OWL. 1-liter stoneware; 9″ (22.9 cm). Similar to *ECS*-124, but a smaller variation. No marks, only the moldmarks # 1662 and 8, GERMANY. Possibly Marzi & Remy (9).

BD-8
EAGLE OWL. ³/₁₀-liter stoneware; 7″ (17.8 cm). Similar to *ECS*-117, except in a smaller version. Marked M. Sch & Co. Ulm Muster Geschützt 18.

BD-9
OWL. ½-liter stoneware; 8¼″ (21 cm). Another proud salt-glaze standing night bird. Its head is brownish-grey; it has a brown feathered body standing above a green base. The pedestal base is surrounded by a single jeweled rim, flutings below. Marked Reinhold Merkelbach (5a), number 147.

Clowns and Jesters

CL-1
NUREMBERG JUDGE. ½-liter porcelain; 7¼″ (18.4 cm). Similar to *ECS*-307, except in the more unusual blue/white onion pattern. Occasionally seen on the Goat (*ECS*-66), Sad Radish (*ECS*-258), and others. Marked Musterschutz (10a).*

CL-2
CLOWN. ½-liter porcelain; 6″ (15.2 cm). This rare stein is probably one of the more beautiful examples of the artistry associated with the marks of Musterschutz (10a) and the crosshatch. The # 97, 7 has been noted on some pieces. (1a).*

*Made by Schierholz and Sohn.

111

CL-3

CLOWN. 2-liter stoneware; 14½″ (36.8 cm). This large pouring vessel is another in the series of quality humorous steins manufactured by the company utilizing the markings D.R.G.M. 154927 (3), moldmark # 751. The twin rear panels read: "*Wer nicht liebt trinkt und singt, Es nie zur wahren Freude bringt.*" (Those who seek what joy can bring, Must learn to love and drink and sing.) Marked GESETZLICH GESCHÜTZT, GERMANY.

CL-4

SMILING CLOWN. ½-liter stoneware; 10¾″ (27.3 cm). A possible mate to the next two steins. Even though there are no marks, the mold # 749 would indicate that it might be D.R.G.M. 154927 (3).

CL-5

JESTER. ½-liter stoneware; 10¾″ (27.3 cm). A comical leer appears on the ruddy face of this piece. The twin rear panels read: "*Sō lang ich lebe, will ich trinken*" and "*Und wenn ich stirb in Fass versinken.*" (Since drinking is my life-long task, What better tomb than this void cask.) Marked D.R.G.M. 154927 (3), GESETZLICH GESCHÜTZT, GERMANY, moldmark # 794 B.

CL-6

SAD JESTER. ½-liter stoneware; 9″ (22.9 cm). This multicolored stein is one of a series of jesters manufactured by D.R.G.M. 154927 (3). Moldmark # 746. For others see *ECS*-311, 312, 313.

CL-7

SMILING JESTER. ½-liter stoneware; 9″ (22.9 cm). A fine mate to the prior stein. Once again this multicolored piece exhibits the jeweled beading along the base often found on the D.R.G.M. 154927 (3) steins. Moldmark # 747, GERMANY.

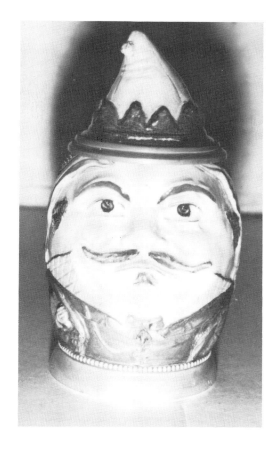

CL-8

JESTER. ¼-liter stoneware; 5½″ (14 cm). A miniature mate to pouring stein *ECS*-311. No marks, only the moldmark # 720. GESETZLICH GESCHÜTZT GERMANY. Typical beaded base ala D.R.G.M. 154927 (3).

CL-9

JESTER. 2-liter stoneware; 17″ (43.2 cm). This very large master stein is another in the series of steins marked D.R.G.M. 154927 (3), moldmark # 753.

CL-10

JESTER. ½-liter stoneware; 11″ (27.9 cm). The same stein as *ECS*-314, except here it appears with a full jester's cap. Marked D.R.G.M. 154927 (3), GERMANY, moldmark # 750.

CL-11

MAN WITH JESTER'S CAP. ¼-liter stoneware; 6½″ (16.5 cm). A smaller version of *ECS*-312. This multicolored piece has two rear panels reading: *"Ein Leid und Leben"* and *"Nach Einheit Streben."* (Though life be filled with pain, Let unity be your aim.) No marks, only the moldmark # 791. GESETZLICH GESCHÜTZT. Probably D.R.G.M. 154927 (3).

CL-12

CLOWN. ⅛-liter stoneware; 4″ (10.2 cm). This small colorless stein may have been used by children for Kinder Bier. The two oval side panels are inscribed: *"Der Lieben Kinder"* and *"Zum wohl sein."* (To the well-being of our dear children.) The moldmark # 167 appears beneath the handle. No pewter attachments. No marks.

CL-13
JESTER. ½-liter stoneware; 8½″ (21.6 cm). This brightly colored stein is marked HR 44 (in black ink), along with the incised number 53 on its bottom. It is felt that HR refers to the decorator and has nothing to do with HR steins made by Hauber & Reuther.

CL-14
JESTER. ½-liter stoneware, 7″ (17.8 cm). Blue/grey in coloring. This jovial, pudgy-faced fellow has a smug smile as his head gazes out of the blue hood. *"Bock mit Rettig"* (Bock [beer] with radish) is inscribed on his chest. Marked Simon Peter Gerz (8a), moldmark # 305.

CL-15
CLOWN. ½-liter stoneware; 10″ (25.4 cm). Similar to *ECS-316*, except in a blue/grey coloring. No marks, only the moldmark # 987. Identified as Reinhold Hanke (18). See "Old Catalogs."

Famous People

FP-1
UNCLE SAM. ½-liter porcelain; 7¼″ (18.4 cm). A rare red, white, and blue version of *ECS-143A*. Marked Musterschutz (10a) and the crosshatch mark (1a).*

FP-2
UNCLE SAM. ½-liter porcelain; 7¼″ (18.4 cm). Beige and brown version of *ECS-143A*. One version has been seen with a wider hat band with 3 rows of stripes instead of 2. Marked Musterschutz (10a) and the crosshatch mark (1a).*

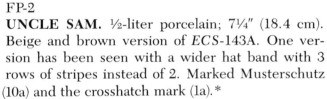

FP-3
BISMARCK. ½-liter porcelain; 7″ (17.8 cm). Similar to the brown/beige *ECS-132*. However, this rarer version appears in a blue/white coloration. Marked Musterschutz (10a).*

FP-4
BISMARCKS. ½-liter porcelain. 7″ (17.8 cm). Three variations of *ECS*-132. From left, blue/white, full color, and brown/beige. All marked Musterschutz (10a).*

FP-5
BISMARCK. ½-liter porcelain; 7″ (17.8 cm). Another variation of the previously described piece. Here it appears in full color. Marked Musterschutz (10a).*

FP-6, 7
WILHELM II. ½-liter porcelain, 8¼″ (21 cm). Two variations of *ECS*-150. On the left is the seldom seen enameled full color version. The other is the beige/brown piece. Marked Musterschutz (10a).*

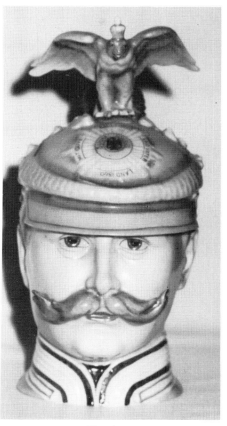

*Made by Schierholz and Sohn.

FP-6

FP-7

117

FP-8
WILHELM I. ½-liter stoneware; 7½" (19.1 cm). Similar to *ECS*-149, but in a blue/grey coloration, and a narrower sash. No marks, only the moldmark #809. Identified as Marzi & Remy (9). See "Old Catalogs."

FP-9
FRIEDRICH III. ½-liter stoneware; 7½" (19.1 cm). Likeness of Kaiser Friedrich III, who reigned for ninety-nine days in 1888, before succumbing to cancer of the throat. He was succeeded to the throne by his son Wilhelm II. Dress uniform is that of a general of cavalry. The headdress is a hussar's fur busby. No marks, only the moldmark #932. Identified as Marzi & Remy (9). See "Old Catalogs."

FP-10
KING LUDWIG OF BAVARIA. ½-liter stoneware; 8½" (16.5 cm). This beige/brown piece depicts Ludwig in the dress uniform of General of the Bavarian Armies. He is attired in the model 1870 Bavarian officer's helmet which was in use through 1890. Under the large fur comb, or helmet crest ("caterpillar") appears a large script "L" for Ludwig. No marks only the incised moldmark #935 over 16. Identified as Marzi & Remy (9).

FP-11
KING LUDWIG II OF BAVARIA, 1845–1886.

FP-12, 13
VON MOLTKE. ½-liter stoneware; 8½″ (21.6 cm). Two renditions of the "young" Von Moltke. Notice the subtle differences in the sashes. The lids (busts) are very similar, although the bodies vary. Varying lids and bases occur because the lids and bases were made separately and then brought together for assembly. No marks, only the incised moldmark #809. Occasionally marked #933. Identified as Marzi & Remy (9.)

FP-12

FP-13

FP-14

VON MOLTKE. ½-liter stoneware; 8½″ (21.6 cm). Similar to *ECS*-146, except for the cream coloring. No marks, only #585. Identified as Reinhold Hanke (18). See "Old Catalogs."

FP-15

FRIEDRICH JAHN. ½-liter porcelain; 6¼″ (15.9 cm). Very similar to *ECS*-141, however, this piece shows Jahn in a reddish-brown cap. Marked Musterschutz (10a).*

FP-16

JAHN. 1-liter porcelain; 7½″ (19.1 cm). A beige/white variation of *ECS*-142. The wreath atop his head is replaced with a beige cap (which is not original, nor correct). Marked Musterschutz (10a).*

FP-17

JAHN. ½-liter; 1-liter porcelain. The beige/brown *ECS*-141 alongside the larger stein. Both are marked Musterschutz (10a).*

*Made by Schierholz and Sohn.

Figurals

FI-1
TURKISH PEASANT. ½-liter porcelain; 9″ (22.9 cm). Very similar to the beige/brown *ECS*-161, except in full color. Marked Musterschutz (10a) and the crosshatch mark (1a).*

FI-2
TURKISH PEASANT. The full color version alongside the beige/brown. Notice the slightly different angulations of the head. Both are marked Musterschutz (10a) and the crosshatch mark (1a).*

FI-3
SLEEPING HUNTER. ½-liter porcelain; 7″ (17.8 cm). Full color rendition of *ECS*-164. No marks.

*Made by Schierholz and Sohn.

FI-4
ALPINE MOUNTAINEER. ½-liter porcelain; 8¼″ (21 cm). Similar to *ECS-165*, except in full color. Marked Musterschutz (10a) and the cross-hatch mark (1a).*

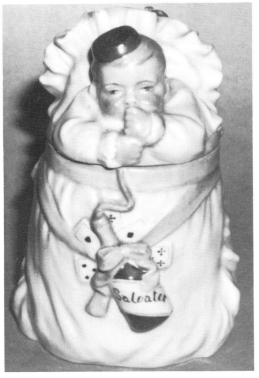

FI-6
BABY. ½-liter porcelain; 7¾″ (19.7 cm). This rosy-cheeked child is very busy sucking a straw from a bottle marked "Salvater" (a strong Bavarian beer). Five cards are tucked behind the bottle, which is dangling from a pink ribbon. The handle is formed of the same ribbons. Marked Musterschutz (10a).*

FI-5
SLEEPING HUNTER. ½-liter porcelain; 7″ (17.8 cm). The beige/brown and full color variations. No marks.

*Made by Schierholz and Sohn.

122

FI-7
DUTCH GIRL and DUTCH BOY. ½-liter porcelain. 8½″ (21.6 cm). Similar to *ECS*-166, however, this beautiful, gentle pair is colored a very subtle blue/grey and white. Marked Musterschutz (10a).*

FI-8
TYROLEAN HUNTER. ½-liter porcelain; 7″ (17.8 cm). This gentleman is using his binoculars to spot the game. Notice the face of a fox in his muff. Marked H. Hutschenreuther (31).

FI-8

FI-9

FI-9
HUNTER. ½-liter stoneware; 8½″ (21.6 cm). This bluish-grey, salt-glazed man carries a blue and brown rifle and a powder keg under his elbow. No marks.

123   *Made by Schierholz and Sohn.

FI-10
ALPINE HUNTER. ½-liter stoneware; 7¾″ (19.7 cm). A greyish-green and brown bulbous man, holding a pipe in his right hand and a rifle draped over his shoulder. A knapsack has the head of a small deer peering out of one side, a rabbit from the other. A pouch on his left shoulder has a bird hanging on the outside. Marked Reinhold Merkelbach (5a). Moldmark # 236.

FI-11
MAN. ½-liter stoneware; 9″ (22.9 cm). Another of many steins showing a figure sitting atop a barrel. His hat forms the lid. The German verse reads: *"Die Frau trinkt die Limonadidös* (Bavarian dialect) *Bier trinke ich."* (My wife enjoys her lemonade; I drink beer in the evening's shade.) The dialect is meant to reflect the Bavarian's attitude. No marks, only the moldmark # 738 GESETSCH. Possibly Reinhold Merkelbach (5a).

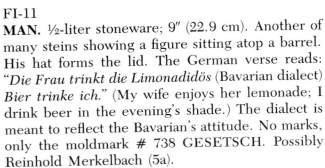

FI-12
MAN. ½-liter earthenware; 7¼″ (18.4 cm). Possible mate to *ECS-225*. No marks, only the moldmark # 1044. GES. GESCHÜTZT.

FI-13

MAN WITH DERBY. ½-liter stoneware; 8¼″ (21 cm). Full-figure of smiling man. The two rear panels are inscribed: "*Wer nicht liebt trinkt und singt,*" and "*es nie Zur wahren Freude bringt.*" (Those who seek what joy can bring must learn to love and drink and sing.) This piece resembles the "Bartender," *ECS*-224. The single beading along the baseline is indicative of the markings D.R.G.M. 154927 (3) GESETZLICH GES-CHÜTZT, moldmark # 764 B.

FI-14

MAN. ½-liter stoneware; 7″ (17.8 cm). Full-figured rich man. He sports a top hat and medalled cutaway coat. Body is similar to FI-15. Same lid also appears on a simpler body. No marks, only # 97 and the "Edelweiss" (30) mark.

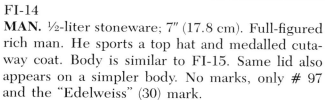

FI-15

PIRATE. ½-liter stoneware, 8¼″ (21 cm). Smiling, salt-glazed pirate. No marks, only # 55.

FI-16
GERMANIC WARRIOR. ½-liter stoneware; 9″ (22.9 cm). A full-color variation of *ECS-157*. The shield reads: "*Die alten Deutschen tranken noch eins.*" (The Germans of yesteryear drank more than their fill of beer!) The text was taken from an old German drinking song, one popular among the *Korporationen* (fraternities) of the universities. It refers to the Germanic warriors of the period from A.D. 50 to 200. Tacitus was a famous Roman historian of the late first and early second centuries A.D. He wrote of his encounters with the Teutons (Germanic tribes). This stein was inspired by the poem by Scheffel. For more information, please refer to the article by Art Maethner on the "Schlitt murals in the Wiesbaden Rathaus" in the September 1976 issue of *Prosit*, 45: 349. Marked GERMANY. Moldmark # 1165. Possibly Steinzeugwerke (23).

FI-17
ADMIRAL. ½-liter stoneware; 7¾″ (19.7 cm). Appearing like a character from an old Gilbert and Sullivan opera. This blue, grey, and brown officer wears a black hat. No marks, only the incised letters gH and the black-lettered # 52.

FI-18
MINER. ½-liter stoneware; 9″ (22.9 cm). A companion to *ECS-218*. This figure carries a stein in his right hand, a brown and yellow lantern in his left. His black cap has the crossed hammer and awl logo of the miner. No marks, only moldmark # 1241.

FI-19
ENGLISH GENTLEMAN. 1-liter earthenware; 10¼″ (26 cm). Appearing similar to a toby mug, this full-figured piece has a lid formed by his hat. The lid separation is between the brim and body of the hat. He holds a paper in his left hand that says "BUDGET." Another paper by his left foot says "Mr. Income." No pewter assembly. No marks.

FI-20
BOWLER. ½-liter stoneware; 9″ (22.9 cm). No marks, only # 1226.

FI-21
MAN READING NEWSPAPER. ½-liter stoneware; 7½″ (19.1 cm). This stern-faced gentleman peers intently at his paper, called "Kölnische Zeitung" (Cologne newspaper). The back page is incised with the date 1886 no. 10, I.D. No marks, only the moldmark #871. Identified as Reinhold Hanke (18). See "Old Catalogs."

FI-22

WIZARD. ½-liter stoneware; 7¼″ (18.4 cm). Astrology dates to ancient times. This soothsayer is garbed in a blue, beige, and brown turban, with a matching star-speckled sash. A beige "man-in-the moon" logo appears on his left breast. The mold-mark # 389 appears under the handle. Marked Merkelbach & Wick (4a).

FI-23

SMILING MIKADO. ½-liter stoneware; 9″ (22.9 cm). This happy beige/ivory Chinese man holds a fan in his right hand. The blue inscription around his midriff reads: *Humor nur "überall ist allemal mein Fall."* (Tis humor I find which gladdens my mind.) No marks. Identified as Reinhold Hanke (18). See "Old Catalogs," # 987. Moldmark # 1081 seen on one specimen.

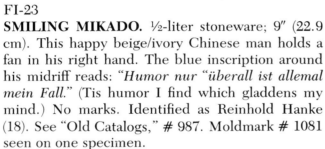

FI-24

FALSTAFF. ½-liter stoneware; 6½″ (16.5 cm). Blue/grey in coloring. A dagger dangles from his belt. Also manufactured in cream and full coloring. Marked Merkelbach & Wick (4a).

AN-2　Berlin Bears

AN-4　Berlin Bear

AN-5　Berlin Bear

AN-5　Detail

AN-22　Poodle

AN-31　Gentleman Fox

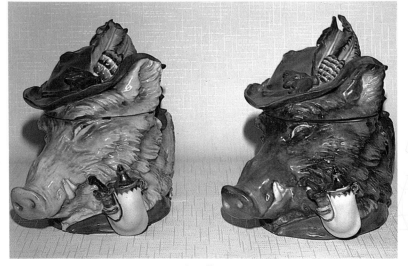

AN-6　Boars

AN-34   Lion

AN-35   Sitting Lion

AN-39   Orangutan

AN-40   Sitting Monkey

AN-46   Pig

AN-47   Seated Goat

AN-49   Goat

AT-2   Barbells

AT-3   Bowling Pins

AT-4   Bowling Balls

AT-5   Bowling Pin

AT-11   Bowling Pins

AT-21   Football

AT-25   Football

AT-32   Football

BD-1   Indian Chief Owl

BD-6   Owl

CL-1   Nuremberg Judge

BD-3   Owl with Jester's Cap

CL-6, 7   Sad Jester; Smiling Jester

CL-3   Clown

CL-2   Clown

FP-1   Uncle Sam

FP-3   Bismarck

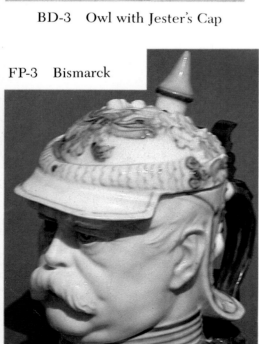

FP-4   Bismarcks

FP-15   Friedrich Jahn

FP-10   King Ludwig of Bavaria

FI-1   Turkish Peasant

FI-3   Sleeping Hunter

FP-6   Wilhelm II

FI-7   Dutch Girl and Dutch Boy

FI-4   Alpine Mountaineer

FI-6   Baby

FI-12   Man

FI-16   Germanic Warrior

FI-20   Bowler

FI-22   Wizard

FI-40   Snowman

FI-35   Fireman

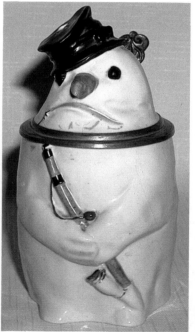

FI-25   Falstaff

FI-41   Gymnasium Teacher

FI-36   Knight

FI-44   Gambrinus

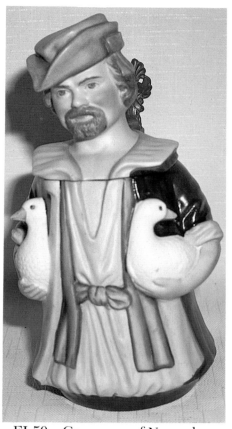

FI-50   Gooseman of Nuremberg

FI-53   Man Astride Barrel

FI-64   Bavarian
Woman and Man

FI-59   Hanswurst

FI-67   Dutch Girl

FI-55   Black Man

FI-61   Madonna

FI-70   Bavaria

HD-1   Trainmaster

HD-4   Hops Lady

HD-10   Egyptian Ladies

HD-5   Smiling Woman

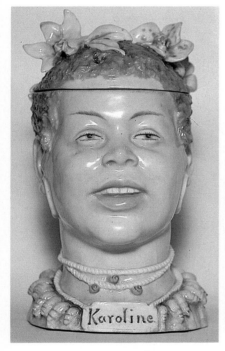

HD-6   Karoline

HD-8, 9   Mother-in-Law; Father-in-Law

HD-14   Man with Duck in M

HD-12   Caroline

HD-16   Our John

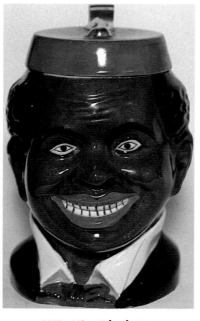

HD-17   Black Man

HD-23   Man with Flower

HD-25   Radish

HD-27   Sad Radish

MT-2   Chinese-German Officer

MT-4   Enlisted Man

MT-7   German CPO

HD-21   Fisherman

MT-10   Artillery Shells

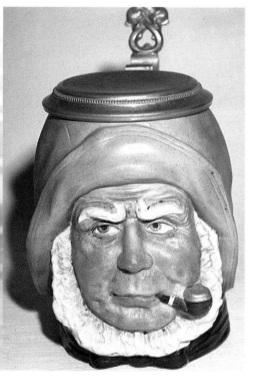

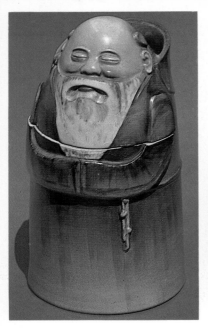

MO-7   Monk

MO-9   Nun

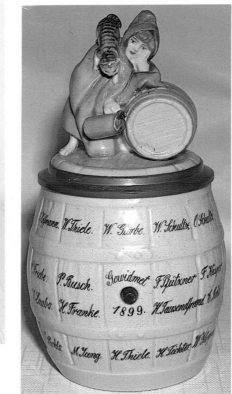

MC-1   Barrel

MC-32   Munich Chi'

MO-10, 11   Monks

Wer Bier trinkt
schläft gut,
wer gut schläft
sündiget nicht
wer nicht sündigt
kommt in den
Himmel

Ein gut Gewissen
Das best Ruhkissen

MC-34   Munich Child

MC-42   Munich Ch'

MC-24, 25   Munich Children

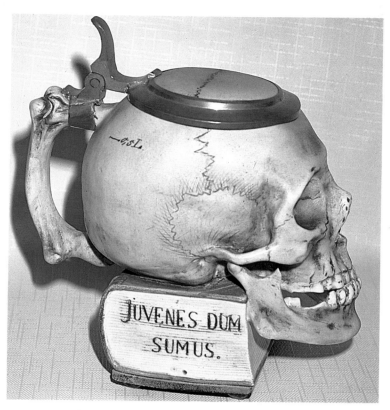

SK-7   Skull on Book

TO-11   East Berlin Town Hall

TO-19   Tower

WA-2   Frogs

WA-1   Fish

WA-4   Frog; Frog on Book

SR-1   Nuremberg Funnel Goblet

MI-20   Mountain

MI-7   Innkeeper

SR-36   Satan Cigar and Matchholder

MI-9   Globe

MI-15   Taxes Tankard

MI-22   Christopher
Columbus

SR-44   Indian Chief
Matchholder

FI-25

FALSTAFF. ½-liter stoneware; 9″ (22.9 cm). Sir John Falstaff was a character who appeared in Shakespeare's *Merry Wives of Windsor* and in the first and second parts of *King Henry IV*. He is exhibited as fat, jovial, humorous, sensual, and cowardly, but with wonderful resources of wit and impudence. Stein also made in a cream and blue coloring. No marks, only the incised moldmark #1439 GERMANY. Identified as Steinzeugwerke (23). See "Old Catalogs."

FI-26
Sir John Falstaff.

FI-27
A shipment of *Falstaff* steins was made for Eaton's, large Canadian department store.

FI-28
RICH MAN. ½-liter stoneware; 7″ (17.8 cm). This smiling, cream colored, muttonchop-bearded gentleman is nattily attired in a colorful robe. The lining is a decorative edelweiss pattern. The matched cap has a small tassel dangling along the side. No marks, only the moldmark # 722, 26. Also seen with moldmark number 8669.

FI-29
RICH MAN. ½-liter stoneware; 7″ (17.8 cm). Similar to the prior stein, except in blue/grey stoneware. No marks, only # 8667 GERMANY.

FI-30
RICH MAN. ½-liter stoneware; 7¼″ (18.4 cm). Almost a "twin" to the previous pieces. In this version the smiling man holds a stein in his right hand. Flowered robe. No marks, only the incised moldmark # 722.

FI-31
MAN WITH BERET. ½-liter stoneware; 7″ (17.8 cm). This blue/grey salt-glaze piece resembles *ECS*- 198 although the base on this stein is plainer. No marks, only moldmark # 461. Identified as Reinhold Hanke (18).

FI-32
KNIGHT. ½-liter stoneware; 7¾″ (19.7 cm). This grey salt-glazed cavalier is perched on a pedestal base. No marks, only # 746. Identified as Marzi & Remy (9). See "Old Catalogs."

FI-33
FIREMAN. ½-liter stoneware; 7¼″ (18.4 cm). Similar in appearance to *ECS*-216. However, this cream and black figural's face is more youthful. No marks, only moldmark # 466. Identified as Reinhold Hanke (18). See "Old Catalogs."

FI-34
MAN. 1-liter stoneware; 8¾″ (22.2 cm). This grey figure is in the shape of a bowling pin. The rim of the lid acts as a gag. The large blue writing says: "*Ich Sag Nix* (dialect—*Nichts*) *Mehr.*" (I won't say anything more.) Was he really out kegling tonight? Marked J. REINEMANN MÜNCHEN (13a).

FI-35

FIREMAN. ½-liter stoneware; 8″ (20.3 cm). A comical companion to *ECS*-216 and 217. The blue/grey figure has a rope encircling his right shoulder. An ax dangles from his belt. No marks, only mold-mark # 750. Identified as Marzi & Remy (9). See "Old Catalogs."

FI-36

KNIGHT. 2-liter earthenware; 14½″ (36.8 cm). Similar to *ECS*-248–51. Again with plumed helmet and atop a pedestal base. Blue and green coloring. No marks.

FI-37

KNIGHT. ½-liter earthenware; 9½″ (24.1 cm). This pouring vessel is adorned with an interesting pewter lid in the shape of a helmet. Inscribed: *"Willst du Wein Schenk dir ein."* (If you wish wine, take some of mine.) No marks.

FI-38

KNIGHT. 1-liter stoneware; 11″ (27.9 cm). Similar to *ECS-247–48*. This bulbous salt-glazed piece is characterized by a somewhat plainer pedestal base. Coloring varies from cobalt blues to greys and browns. No pewter attachment. The inscription reads: *"Trink u. iss Gott nit vergiss."* (Though wined and dined, keep God in mind.) Marked Merkelbach & Wick (4a).

FI-39

KNIGHT. 1½-liter stoneware; 13″ (33 cm). Similar to the prior piece. Coloration is a salt-glazed blue and grey. The frontal panel says: *"Dieser Krug ist gemacht Dass man jubelt u. lacht. Doch in geheimer Kamer Schläft Katzenjamer."* (This stalwart mug was designed with pleasure in mind. Yet in its hidden chamber lurks everpresent danger.) No marks.

FI-40

SNOWMAN. ½-liter porcelain; 8¼″ (21 cm). Full-color version of *ECS-184*. This is the more common stein seen, the blue and white variation is quite rare. Marked Musterschutz (10a).*

*Made by Schierholz and Sohn.

FI-41

GYMNASIUM TEACHER. ½-liter stoneware; 8″ (20.3 cm). This bearded professor is in the act of reminding his pupils that they have *Fünf Minuten* (five minutes) left to complete their final examination *(Abitur)*. He has just pushed his reading glasses up in order to keep a sharp eye on his charges during this last crucial segment of time. The official timepiece on his scholarly vest will shortly sound the alarm and signal an end to his pupils' ordeal. No marks, only the moldmark # 697. GESETZLICH GESCHÜTZT GERMANY. Possibly D.R.G.M. 154927 (3).

(We thank Art Maethner for this interesting interpretation)

FI-42
Gambrinus is my name,
and beer is my fame.

Gambrinus

The legendary German King of Beer (or lager) is an individual named Gambrinus, sometimes referred to as Saint Gambrinus. This robust figure, always depicted holding a mug, stein, or glass of brew, is quite often portrayed on beer steins.

Who was this mysterious figure? At least one of the early historians states that Gambrinus was born in 1730 B.C., exactly 2,234 years after the creation of the world. A much more plausible theory about the legend points to a man who actually lived—one portrait of Gambrinus labels him as "King of Flanders and Brabant." We do know that a famous Baron of Brabant was a certain Jan Primus, who was not only a noted warrior and a local hero, but was also renowned for his drinking capacity. He is said to have quaffed seventy-two quarts of beer at one sitting! In addition, he was president of the Brussels Guild of Brewers from 1261 to 1294. If one says "Jan Primus" fast enough and figures that a man of that name was the champion drinker of his time, and a brewer as well, one has the right kind of start to launch a patron saint of beer: Gambrinus.

FI-43
GAMBRINUS. ¼-liter stoneware; 6¼″ (15.9 cm). This sitting king holds an open stein in his right hand, a scepter in his left. Leaves and plants surround his tiny feet. A jeweled base such as is found on many D.R.G.M. 154927 (3) steins. Moldmark # 727.

FI-44
GAMBRINUS. 3-liter stoneware; 16½″ (41.9 cm). A very large mate to the previously described figural. The stein he holds has the word *"Prosit"* written on its side. This bulbous pouring piece narrows to a single-jeweled base. Marked D.R.G.M. 154927 (3), moldmark. # 726, GERMANY GESETZLICH GESCHÜTZT.

FI-45
BEARDED CAVALIER. 3-liter stoneware; 15½″ (39.4 cm). A large blue/grey figural master stein. The unattached lid is formed by his hat. The verse across his portly stomach reads: *"Heben trinken allzuviel, Schadet sei es wie es will."* (Though harm may come to such a man, he lifts and drinks as much as he can). No marks, only moldmark # 203 is incised into the bottom. Identified as Reinhold Hanke (18). See "Old Catalogs."

FI-46
KENTUCKY COLONEL. 3-liter stoneware; 13½″ (34.3 cm). The late Colonel Sanders would have been mighty proud to have sipped some southern brew out of this fine blue/grey piece. The small pedestal base is encased in a pewter rim. No marks.

FI-47, 48, 49
The **FOUNTAIN OF THE LITTLE GOOSEMAN** (Der Gaensemaennchen Brunnen) is located in the court of the New City Hall, Hauptmarkt 18, Nuremberg, Germany. The famous fountain was cast in bronze by Pankranz Labenwolf (circa 1550).

FI-47

FI-48

FI-49

FI-50
GOOSEMAN OF NUREMBERG. ½-liter porcelain; 9″ (22.9 cm). Similar to *ECS*-175, except this bisque version is very delicately colored. No marks.

FI-51
GOOSEMAN OF NUREMBERG. ½-liter porcelain; 8″ (20.3 cm). This bisque black depiction of the fountain has greenish highlights to give the appearance of weathered bronze. No marks.

FI-52
GOOSEMAN OF NUREMBERG. ½-liter porcelain; 7¾″ (19.7 cm). Same as *ECS*-173. Notice the contrast with the prior steins. Lithophane of city. Marked Musterschutz (10a).*

*Made by Schierholz and Sohn.

137

FI-53
MAN ASTRIDE BARREL. ½-liter earthenware; 11″ (27.9 cm). An unusual multicolored pouring vessel. The "colonist-like" man holds a wine jug in his left hand. The barrel is marked X/VIII on both sides. No marks.

FI-54
CAVALIER. 2-liter stoneware; 17″ (43.2 cm). A very large version of *ECS-156*—obviously comes from the same "family." Marked D.R.G.M. 154927 (3), GESETZLICH GESCHÜTZT, # 733.

FI-54

FI-55
BLACK MAN. ½-liter stoneware; 8¾″ (22.2 cm). A large "HB" stein rests between the legs of this top-hatted minstrel-like figural. The verse around the base says: *"Willst Africa Du cultivieren, so musst Du bairisch Bier einführen."* (If Africa you wish to develop, pour Bavarian beer in every cup.) He sports a red coat and pink tie. No marks, only mold-mark #737 F GESCHÜTZT. Possibly Reinhold Merkelbach (5a).

138

FI-56

FUNNEL MAN. ½-liter stoneware; 9½″ (24.1 cm). Companion piece to *ECS*-192. However, on this version the lid handle attaches to the right side of the funnel-hat. Since steins of that era were not "mass-produced" it is probable that the potters placed the handles indiscriminately. The inscription reads: *"Frau ärgere deinen Mann nicht."* (Woman, don't aggravate your husband.) No marks. Possibly made by Reinhold Hanke (18). See "Old Catalogs."

FI-57

FUNNEL MEN. ½-liter stoneware; 9½″ (24.1 cm). Three variations of *ECS*-192. Notice the position of the.hands of the piece on the left, lying flat on the bulbous stomach. Most examples have the hands extended out. No marks. Possibly made by Reinhold Hanke (18). See "Old Catalogs."

FI-58

SANTA CLAUS. ¼-liter stoneware; 6″ (15.2 cm). This cross-eyed, pin-headed St. Nick has evidently imbibed too much Christmas cheer. The figure may represent the *Weihnachtsmann*, the German equivalent of the American Santa Claus. Similar figures can be purchased in German shops today, though not in the shape of steins.

This figure also may represent *Servant Rupprecht*. In Germany on 6 December children leave their shoes outside the door. If they have been good, they find candy in their shoes left by the "good man." If they are bad, they find lumps of coal left by Rupprecht, the "bad man." This figure seems to be carrying a bag of coal. No marks, only # 1393, GERMANY.

FI-59

HANSWURST. ¼-liter stoneware; 6″ (15.2 cm). A fine addition to the many humorous children's steins seen in *ECS-237*. *Hanswurst* was the name given to that popular clown-like figure of the old German theater. He appeared as *Harlekin* in the Italian comedy-farces of that time. Today he appears as *Kasperl* in German puppet theater presentations. The base inscription reads: *"ICH BIN BE-KANNT IM GANZEN LAND. HANSWURST BIN ICH GENANNT."* (Hanswurst is my name, And fame is my game.) Marked J. REINEMANN MÜNCHEN (13a), GESETZLICH GESCHÜTZT.

FI-60

GRETHL. ¼-liter stoneware; 5¼″ (13.3 cm). This colorful figural holds a glass of beer. The verse along the base says: *"ICH BIN DIE GRETHL—JEDERZEIT ZUM LUSTIG. SEIN und SPASS BE-REIT."* (I am Grethl—always ready for a good time and a little playing around.) Marked J. REINEMANN MÜNCHEN (13a) GESETZ-LICH GESCH.

FI-61

MADONNA. ½-liter stoneware; 7″ (17.8 cm). This "angelic" figure wears a small crown on her head. A heart is held in her right hand. Marked J. REINEMANN MÜNCHEN (13a).

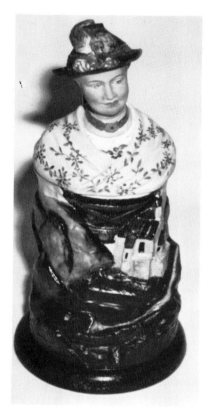

FI-62

BAVARIAN WOMAN. ½-liter porcelain; 10″ (25.4 cm). Similar to *ECS*-169, however, this bisque piece shows an interesting alpine scene around her "skirt" (base). Her lovely smiling face gazes towards her mate. A lithophane shows a scene of a Bavarian chalet, mountains in the background. Marked Jos. M. Mayer München, Bayerstr. 3 (12).

FI-63

BAVARIAN MAN. ½-liter porcelain; 11″ (27.9 cm). A mate to the prior stein. This unusual bisque figural is fairly similar to *ECS*-168. The base also depicts an alpine village. His smiling face peers towards his right. The word "Sepp" (A common Bavarian man's name) is written across his suspenders (on some versions). On one version a lithophane shows a scene of the Zugspitz, Germany's highest mountain, with the inscription *"Osft. Zugspitz Gifei."* Marked Jos. M. Mayer München, Bayerstr. 3. (12) under the handle.

FI-64
BAVARIAN WOMAN AND MAN.

FI-65
BLACK WOMAN. 1-liter stoneware; 9½″ (24.1 cm). This "Aunt Jemima" characterization is holding an umbrella and stein. Marked with a shield and Coblenz, Rheinland. Date of manufacture undetermined.

FI-66
LISL. ½-liter stoneware; 8″ (20.3 cm). This blue/grey barmaid holds a "HB München" stein in each hand. A radish is tucked under her left arm, a bag under her right. The purse hanging across her stomach reads "Lisl." Marked J. REINEMANN, MÜNCHEN (13a), GESETZLICH GESCHÜTZT.

142

FI-67
DUTCH GIRL. ½-liter stoneware; 7½″ (19.1 cm). This lovely cream-colored piece is marked Merkelbach & Wick (4a), GESCHÜTZT, # 685. It also has been identified as having been manufactured by Reinhold Merkelbach (5a). See "Old Catalogs."

FI-68
HOUSEKEEPER. ½-liter stoneware; 7″ (17.8 cm). This blue and grey smiling frau has a key hanging from her robe. Perhaps she is the mistress of a Gasthaus? Her hair is tied into a bun. No marks.

FI-69
BAVARIA UND RUHMESHALLE IN MUNICH.

FI-70
BAVARIA. 1-liter stoneware; 11¼″ (28.6 cm). Very similar to *ECS-240*, however, this version has no pewter rim on the lid. It also stands on a 1″ base upon which is inscribed "BAVARIA." Marked Reinhold Merkelbach (5a).

FI-71

FI-72

FI-73

FI-74

FI-71
LADY WITH BUSTLE. ½-liter wood and pewter; 9¾″ (24.8 cm). Very similar to *ECS*-244, however, the body is a dark wood finish. Her parasol attaches to the handle. No marks.

FI-72
LADY WITH BUSTLE. ½-liter, glass and pewter, 8¼″ (21 cm). Another unusual variation, here the young woman holds a fan, rather than a parasol. Her bustle billows behind her to form the ornate lid. Circa 1886 from the incised inscription. No marks.

FI-73
WOMAN. ½-liter stoneware; 7½″ (19.1 cm). This blue/grey lady is beautifully attired in her blue and black robe. She resembles the "Rich Man," *ECS*-202. Could she be his wife (girl friend)? Also appears in a cream-color variation. Marked Merkelbach & Wick (4a).

FI-74
KELLNERIN. ½-liter stoneware; 9½″ (24.1 cm). A salt-glazed version of *ECS*-219. This blue-grey barmaid stands atop a plain base. No marks, only # 1089. Identified as Reinhold Hanke (18). See "Old Catalogs."

FI-75

FI-75
IRON MAIDEN. ¼-liter pewter; 4¾″ (12.1 cm). The hideous story of the Iron Maiden from Nuremberg is described in *ECS*-239. This small stein is incised along the bottom with D.R.G.M. # 158535.

FI-76

FI-76, 77, 78
MOTHER-IN-LAW. ½-liter stoneware; 6¾″ (17.1 cm). This stern-faced woman holds a large money bag marked "100,000" (marks?). Several other money bags in various denominations surround the handle. The word "*Schwiegermutter*" (Mother-in-law) is incised along the base. John Hamilton cites the book *The Witch of Wall Street* (Doubleday, Doran and Co., 1935), the story of Hetty Green (at one time the richest woman in America), as possibly the model for this unusual stein. Multicolored and cream/green coloration. A nice mate to *ECS*-215. No marks, only the word GERMANY.

FI-77

FI-78 Hetty Green (*left*).

Heads

HD-2
MASKED RACING DRIVER. ½-liter porcelain; 5¾″ (14.6 cm). *ECS*-267. Possibly Ernst Bohne (2).

HD-1
TRAINMASTER. ½-liter porcelain; 6½″ (16.5 cm). A very rare depiction of a civilian railway worker. The uniform and insignia indicate that the official was with the Prussian State Railway, possibly a stationmaster. The name "A. Hedwig" is lettered in black ink on the inside of the white porcelain lid. A gold-leaf winged wheel appears on his cap. Railroad locomotives decorate his Eisenbahn collar. No marks.

HD-3
MASKED RACING DRIVER. 1-liter porcelain; 8½″ (21.6 cm). Similar to *ECS*-267, however, appearing in the larger 1-liter version (alongside the lidless ½-liter stein). The steins are missing the green goggles, which were in effect the racing driver's personal windshield. These goggles were cemented on after the stein was complete. This piece was previously erroneously identified as a "Sulky Driver." However, the ever alert Art Maethner has pointed out that because early "horseless carriages" had no windshields, the driver usually protected his face with some form of mask. No marks, only # 46. Possibly Ernst Bohne (2a).

HD-4
HOPS LADY. ½-liter porcelain; 6″ (15.2 cm). Same stein as *ECS*-288, except in the rare blue and white Meissen coloring. Marked Musterschutz (10a).*

HD-5
SMILING WOMAN. ½-liter porcelain; 7″ (17.8 cm). A finer portrait of *ECS*-293. Marked Musterschutz (10a) and the crosshatch mark (1a).*

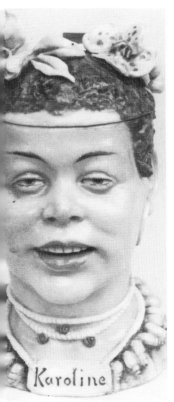

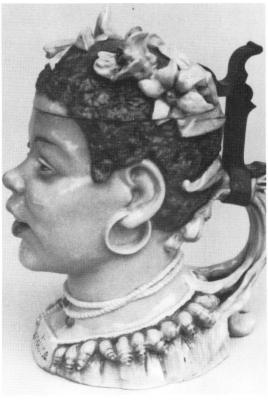

HD-6, 7
KAROLINE. ½-liter porcelain; 7¾″ (19.7 cm). This intriguing beige and rust-toned piece is accented by the delicate orchids in her hair. The legend of Karoline, as stated by Art Maethner, is that her name is the German derivation of Caroline. It is also the name of a group of islands in the South Pacific owned at one time by the Spaniards. They sold these islands to the Germans in 1899. Pictures seen of the islanders reflect the same facial characteristics portrayed on this stein. Although there seems to be a Negroid cast to the features, they are actually Micronesian. Maethner believes that the German designer of this stein meant to portray a native princess of the *Karolinen-Inseln* (Caroline Islands). The use of the orchids as a decoration in her hair and the conche necklace would tend to confirm this assumption. Marked Musterschutz (10a) and the crosshatch mark (1a).*

HD-6   HD-7

*Made by Schierholz and Sohn.

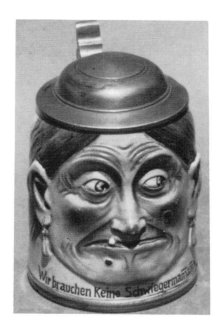

HD-8
MOTHER-IN-LAW. ½-liter stoneware; 5¼″ (13.3 cm). Certainly a joy to any loving son-in-law (?). This single-toothed beauty should visit her local dentist. The expression reads: "*Wir brauchen Keine Schwiegermama.*" (We do not need a mother-in-law.) No marks, only moldmark # 1458, GERMANY GESETZLICHT GESCHÜTZT. Steinzeugwerke (23). See "Old Catalogs" # 1457.

HD-9
FATHER-IN-LAW. ½-liter stoneware; 5½″ (13.3 cm). Being married to the prior "beauty," his intoxicated smile shows he spends a lot of time imbibing. No marks. Possibly Steinzeugwerke (23).

HD-10
EGYPTIAN LADY. ½-liter stoneware; 6″ (15.2 cm). Similar to *ECS-290.* The contemporary on left. The older version, to the right has a lavendar headdress, light brown hair, blue eyes, and gold earrings. Finer details. The left one is marked Eckhardt & Engler Kg. (6a) and moldmark # 431.17. The older one, on the right, is moldmarked # 431 D. Also appears in the Rosskopf & Gerz (38) catalog. See "Old Catalogs."

HD-11
CAROLINE. ½-liter porcelain; 5¼″ (13.3 cm). Similar to *ECS*-292. Her "bonnet" is the pewter lid. The handle is formed by her brown braided hair. No marks. Has been seen marked Musterschutz (10a).* This version is in full color.

HD-12
CAROLINE. ½-liter stoneware; 6½″ (16.5 cm). A similar version of *ECS*-292. No marks, only # 753 GERMANY.

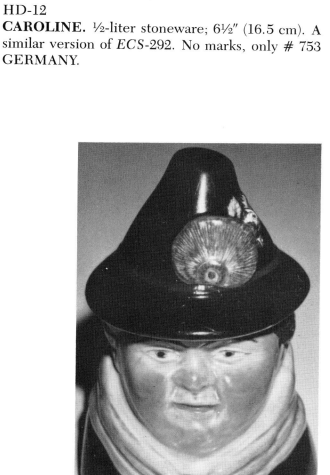

HD-13
TYROLEAN WOMAN. ½-liter earthenware; 6″ (15.2 cm). By the appearance of the purple scarf, this lovely lady can brave the cool Bavarian weather. No marks, only Nachterdach, II. In one version the handle is formed by the braid of her hair. The hat forms the lid and lacks any pewter attachments.

*Made by Schierholz and Sohn.

149

HD-14

MAN WITH DUCK IN MOUTH. ½-liter stoneware; 6¼″ (15.9 cm). Here our boozing friend is so intoxicated, that he believes a feathery duck is stuck in his mouth. His "cracked head" has brains oozing out from both sides. A large poisonous spider sits atop his head. The handle is formed by an open-mouthed snake devouring his own tail. Is beer worth it all? A double-jeweled base indicative of D.R.G.M. 154927 (3). Moldmark # 692 F, GERMANY incised into the base.

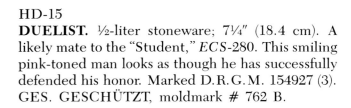

HD-15

DUELIST. ½-liter stoneware; 7¼″ (18.4 cm). A likely mate to the "Student," *ECS*-280. This smiling pink-toned man looks as though he has successfully defended his honor. Marked D.R.G.M. 154927 (3). GES. GESCHÜTZT, moldmark # 762 B.

HD-16

OUR JOHN. ½-liter stoneware; 7¼″ (18.4 cm). This pudgy fellow evidently had a ruckus at the local pub, as his darkened tooth and shiner indicate. A bandanna is wrapped around his aching head. No marks, only the incised moldmark # 1458, GERMANY. This stein has been reproduced recently by Rastal (24) in a 1½ liter size in either porcelain or stoneware. Titled *"Unser Hannes"* (Our John).

HD-17, 18
BLACK MAN. ½-liter porcelain; 6″ (15.2 cm). The glazed porcelain highlights the broad smile and shiny white teeth. The lid is formed by the tasseled red cap. No marks.

HD-19
INDIAN. ½-liter porcelain; 8″ (20.3 cm) to the tip of the feathers. This ruddy-faced Indian looks as though he came right off an old Indian-head nickel. No marks. Possibly contemporary.

HD-20
SMILING FACE. ½-liter stoneware; 5¾″ (14.6 cm). Cylindrical in shape, the colorful face is not painted on the surface, but is part of the stein itself. The #1225 appears below the handle. The same moldmark is incised into the bottom, along with the mark of Simon Peter Gerz (8a).

HD-22
SMILING BLACK MAN. ½-liter stoneware; 5½" (14 cm). This plain stein is hand painted with the face of a pipe-smoking man. He wears gold earrings. The smooth pewter lid appears to be a head covering. No marks.

HD-21
FISHERMAN. ½-liter porcelain; 5¼" (13.3 cm). A similar bisque version of *ECS*-273. This larger piece's face has more lifelike character. Marked Ernst Bohne (2).

HD-23
MAN WITH FLOWER. ½-liter stoneware; 7¼" (18.4 cm). A smiling mate to *ECS*-291, "Coquette." The blue flower clinched in his mouth matches the collar. Green old hat. No marks, except the mold-mark # 765. Identified as J. W. Remy (39). See "Old Catalogs."

HD-24
RADISH. ½-liter porcelain; 7¾″ (19.7 cm). A completely different variation of the many radishes seen in *ECS*. Here the smirking (smiling?) face appears along the side of the base. A beard extends to one side. Coloration is greyish with green leaves on the lid. Marked Ernst Bohne (2c).

HD-25
RADISH. ½-liter stoneware; 7½″ (19.1 cm). This cream-colored piece evidently was designed to characterize both the "happy" and "sad" radishes. Notice how the face appears in a half smile-half frown. No marks, only the moldmark # 1225.

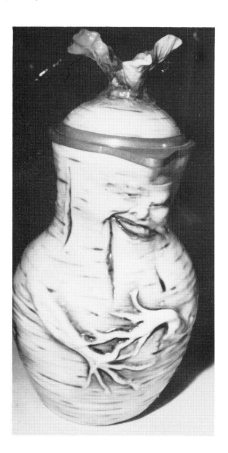

HD-26
RADISH MASTER KRUG. 3-liter porcelain; 12″ (30.5 cm). A rare variation in the blue/white coloration of *ECS-256*. Marked Musterschutz (10a).*

*Made by Schierholz and Sohn.

153

HD-28
SAD RADISHES. ½-liter beige/brown; ½-liter blue/white; ¼-liter beige/brown.

HD-27
SAD RADISH. ½-liter porcelain; 7½″ (19.1 cm). Similar to *ECS*-256, but in the rare blue/white coloring. The basic stein is an off-white, but laced with random blue horizontal striations. The eyes, eyebrows, mouth, and radish leaves are a darker blue coloring. This same blue/white version was also made as a "Happy Radish." Marked Musterschutz (10a).*

HD-29
An early (1899) American patent for a Liberty Head character stein. Although patented, no actual production models have been seen. The New York Stein Collectors International Convention of 1974 featured a similar "Statue of Liberty" commemorative stein. See "Contemporary Steins."

*Made by Schierholz and Sohn.

154

Military

MT-1

ENLISTED MAN. ½-liter stoneware; 9¼″ (23.5 cm). This happy soldier holds a beer stein in his right hand and an alpine pipe in his left, while a flask dangles from his neck. This particular stein has the inscription etched into the pewter lid ring: "Reservist Ströder, served on active duty 1903–5, second Nassau Infantry Regiment # 88, Mainz on the Rhine River." No marks, only moldmark # 1242.

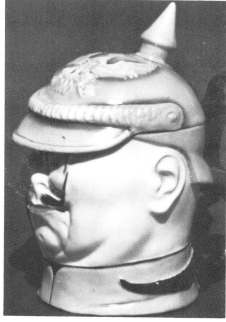

MT-2

MT-2, 3

CHINESE-GERMAN OFFICER. ½-liter porcelain; 6¾″ (17.1 cm). An unusual variation of the Bismarck stein (*ECS-132*). This half-Chinese, half-German face comically blends two cultures into one piece. The Germans occupied the Chinese city of Kiautschau (Tientsin) in the late 1800s. In all probability Chinese soldiers were used in the occupation. The helmet is similar to the 1867-style *Garde* helmet. Black-braided hair appears from the helmet forming the unique handle. Marked Musterschutz (10a) and the crosshatch mark (1a).*

MT-3

155   *Made by Schierholz and Sohn.

MT-4
ENLISTED MAN. ½-liter porcelain; 6″ (15.2 cm). Similar to *ECS*-325. Except the cap is blue and red. The *koller* is a solid red. Notice that all the heads are the same mold, only decorated differently. No marks.

MT-5
ENLISTED MAN. ½-liter porcelain; 6″ (15.2 cm). Similar to *ECS*-325. The markings of his blue and white *muetze* (cap) indicate he is a member of the Saxon Garde Reiter. His mustache and hair are a beige and brown. No marks.

MT-6
ENLISTED MAN. ½-liter porcelain; 5¾″ (14.6 cm). Another variation of the prior stein. The facial expression of this *kurassier* seems to indicate a mild level of intoxication. No marks, only moldmark # 1932 incised.

MT-7
GERMAN CPO. ½-liter stoneware; 8½″ (21.6 cm). A figural of a Chief Petty Officer, wearing his "walking out" uniform, or *bluse* which includes a pillbox-type hat or *Muetze*. Uniform is dark blue with Prussian red piping, symbolizing control by the Kaiser. He carries a sword on his left side and several medals on his chest. Marked T.W. (20a) and the numbers 316 and LB 20.

MT-8
SWISS SOLDIER. ½-liter stoneware; 7″ (17.8 cm). Unidentified bust of a soldier wearing a style of headdress commonly known as a *Raupenhelm* which somewhat resembles an American Civil War soldier's hat. The horsehair plume sweeps around the front of the cap to the side and over the left ear. The "Swiss Cross" is seen on the front of the hat. No marks, only LB & C. GESETZLICH GES-CHÜTZT.

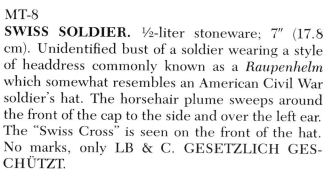

MT-9
ARTILLERY SHELLS. ½-liter stoneware; 10″ (25.4 cm). Two steins similar to *ECS*-335 and 336. The Belgian cities of Lüttich (Liège), Namur, and Antwerpen (Antwerp) and the French cities of Longwy and Maubeuge are written on the pieces. The cities had reenforced concrete and steel cupola-type fortresses which were reduced by the then new German 42 cm howitzer ("Big Bertha") missiles in 1914–15. Both steins commemorate these military successes and their means. No marks, only PA 441546. (Credit to Eugene J. Smith.)

MT-10

ARTILLERY SHELLS. ½-liter porcelain; 9½″ (24.1 cm). Three different color versions of *ECS*-333 and 334. Left—red and grey; middle—blue with orange bands; right—beige with orange pressure bands. The lithophane on the left stein depicts a man and woman sitting. The similar stein to the right shows hunters saying farewell to their women. The center depicts three men sitting around a table playing cards. No marks.

MT-11

MT-10

ARTILLERY SHELL. ½-liter porcelain; 9½″ (24.1 cm). Another variation of *ECS*-333. This version is enhanced by the unusual flaming ball thumblift. No marks. Pewter lid.

MT-12

MT-13

MT-11

MT-12

ARTILLERY SHELL. ½-liter silverplated. A custom-made stein. This was originally a real shell. The medallion on the front reads "Empereur Napoleon III." The lid is formed by the fuse of the missile, with the incised markings of the timing band. Incised in the bottom are the markings Patronen-fabrik Karlsruhe, Sept 1915, St 213, with a small crown and the initials ke 1.

MT-13

ARTILLERY SHELL. Unknown capacity, pewter; 7½″ (19.1 cm). A simple stein with the engraved initial G on the front. A single broad copper band. The name N. G. WOOD & SONS MAKERS BOSTON, MASS. is incised into the base, along with the # 1026. PAT. 14 DEC. 1909.

ℳonks and ℕuns

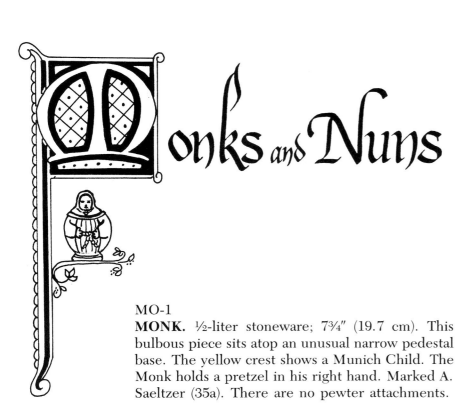

MO-1
MONK. ½-liter stoneware; 7¾″ (19.7 cm). This bulbous piece sits atop an unusual narrow pedestal base. The yellow crest shows a Munich Child. The Monk holds a pretzel in his right hand. Marked A. Saeltzer (35a). There are no pewter attachments.

MO-2
MONK. Silver; 1″ (2.54 cm). No marks.

MO-3
MONK. ¼-liter stoneware; 5½″ (14 cm). A smaller version of MO-6. Notice the interesting pewter cavalier thumblift. No marks, only the # 194.

MO-4
MONK. ½-liter stoneware; 7″ (17.8 cm). Wearing a fancy decorated robe, this blue/grey jovial smiling monk is another in a large group of bulbous monks. No marks.

MO-5
SMILING MONK. 1-liter stoneware; 8½″ (21.6 cm). Similar to *ECS*-339, however, this stein has a bronze lid. Marked Merkelbach & Wick (4a).

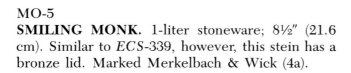

MO-6
MONK. 1-liter salt-glaze stoneware; 11″ (27.9 cm). A very large variation of the many monks manufactured with large bulbous bodies (see *ECS*-339, 351). The purplish-grey body is similar to *ECS*-341. CA. 1883. No marks only moldmark # 194.

MO-7
MONK. ½-liter stoneware. 8½″ (21.6 cm). An almost oriental-looking monk. His open hood lies behind his docile face. No marks, only moldmark # 1304, GERMANY.

MO-8
GRINNING MONK. ½-liter stoneware; 7¼″ (18.4 cm). Jolly monk with white hair and brick-red robe. Marked HR 14 in ink. Not an HR mark, but believed to be the decorator's initials. Similar to *ECS-344*. No marks.

MO-9
NUN. ½-liter stoneware; 7½″ (19.1 cm). Mate to the prior monk. Marked HR 33 in black ink. Once again the initials of the decorator. No marks.

MO-10
MONK. ¼-liter stoneware; 6¼" (15.9 cm). This jovial monk holds a pouring stein in his right hand, a radish tucked under his arm. His left holds a sign reading: *"Ein gut Gewissen Das best Ruhkissen."* (A conscience clear is without peer and helps us all asleep to fall.) A bag is slung over the left arm. Sandaled feet stick out from below his robe. No marks, only moldmark # 654. A possible mate to *ECS*-360. Probably made by Dümler & Breiden (19).

MO-11
MONK. ½-liter stoneware, 7¼" (18.4 cm); ¼-liter stoneware, 6¼" (15.9 cm). *ECS*-360 (left) alongside the previously described piece. The banner reads: *"Wer Bier trinkt, Schläft gut, Wer gut schläft sündiget nicht. Wer nicht sündigt kommt in den Himmel."* (Those who drink are sure to sleep, those who sleep commit no sin, and, therefore, they can heaven win.) No marks, only moldmark # 572 on the left. Made by Dümler & Breiden (19).

MO-12
MONK. ½-liter porcelain; 6¾" (17.1 cm). This brown-robed portly monk wears a black skullcap. A large lithophane encompasses the entire bottom. The saying on the lithophane is: *"Ein volles Glas, Ein braves Weib, Ein frohes Lied, Erhält den Leib."* (A glass filled with beer, A woman so dear, A song of good cheer, uphold us all here.) Fancy scrollwork appears above and below the lithophane. This stein was made with a variety of lithophanes. No marks.

MO-13
MONK AND NUN. The previously described
Monk along with Nun (*ECS*-364).

Munich Childs

MC-1

MC-1
BARREL. ½-liter porcelain; 8″ (20.3 cm). Similar to the stein shown as *ECS-397*. However, this piece is covered with various men's names lettered in black script. Around the *pung* is written "*Gewidmet 1899,*" (Dedicated 1899). The handle is formed in the shape of a fish. The handle very often is seen in the shape of a radish (MC-2). The lithophane shows a city scene. Marked Musterschutz (10a) with the crosshatch mark (1a).*

*Made by Schierholz and Sohn.

MC-2

164

MC-3
MUNICH CHILD. Stoneware; 1-liter, 10″ (25.4 cm); ½-liter, 7¾″ (19.7 cm); ¼-liter, 6½″ (16.5 cm); ⅛-liter, 5⅜″ (13.5 cm); ¹⁄₁₆-liter, 4½″ (11.4 cm). The entire "family" of polychrome steins is shown here. A detailed description of the "pale-faced" (un-colored) Child can be found by *ECS*-374. Some are marked J. REINEMANN MÜNCHEN (13a and 13b). The ½-liter size has been seen with the mold-mark # 209. Also marked GESETZLICH GES-CHÜTZT.

MC-4
MUNICH CHILD. ½-liter stoneware; 7¾″ (19.7 cm). A closer look at the "pale-faced" Child. Marked J. REINEMANN, MÜNCHEN (13a).

MC-5

MUNICH CHILD. Stoneware; from left: ¹⁄₁₆-liter, 4½″ (11.4 cm); ⅛-liter, 5⅜″ (13.5 cm); ¼-liter, 6¼″ (15.9 cm); ½-liter 7¾″ (19.7 cm); 1-liter, 10″ 25.4 cm). This is the so-called colored face series (as opposed to the "pale-faced series"). Coloring of the robe, steins, radishes, etc. are the same as in the previous descriptions. However, in this group the facial features are very lifelike (e.g., blue eyes, rosy cheeks, skin-tones, etc.). Glazed. Notice that all the smaller steins are peering to their left. The larger 1-liter looks straight forward. This is similar in the "pale-faced series." Marked-J. REINEMANN, MÜNCHEN (13a). GESETZ-LICH GESCHÜTZT. One version of the 1-liter stein is marked L. LICHTINGER, MÜNCHEN on the base instead of J. REINEMANN.

MC-6

MUNICH CHILD. Porcelain; ¼-liter, 6¼″ (15.9 cm). This polychrome is a typical Reinemann design. "HB MÜNCHEN" stein in right hand, radishes in left hand and under arm. Pewter rimmed lid with filigreed thumblift, black robe and hood, gold lining; yellow/orange scapular. Lifelike face (blue eyes, red lips, pink cheeks, brown hair). The bottom script inscription is incised into the base. J. REINEMANN, MÜNCHEN (13).

MC-7

MUNICH CHILD. Porcelain; ⅛-liter, 5″ (12.7 cm); ½-liter, 7¾″ (19.7 cm). A pair of similar steins. The Child holds a large grey stein marked "HB *Gruss aus München*," (Greetings from Munich). The other hand clasps a single radish; two are tucked under the arm. The larger Child has a pewter rim. The basic stein is finished in a heavy-glazed porcelain, except for a well-detailed bisque face. A likeness to *ECS*-390, which is in stoneware. No marks. The steins are similar to the previous one.

MC-8

MUNICH CHILD. Porcelain; ⅛-liter, 5″ (12.7 cm); ¼-liter 6¼″ (15.9 cm); ½-liter, 7¾″ (19.7 cm). A group picture showing the previous three steins. Notice similarity in workmanship. Even though the ⅛-liter and ½-liter are unsigned, they are sufficiently similar to warrant the assumption that they all were made for J. Reinemann München (13).

MC-9

MUNICH CHILD. ½-liter stoneware; 8¼″ (21cm). The Child grasps a cream-colored stein in both hands. Radishes are tucked under both arms. The Bavarian rhombus crest (blue and white diamond pattern) at bottom under scapula. A pewter rim encircles lid, inside of which is a pewter sheet to cover the head cavity. The face is cream, as are the hands and radishes. The black robe is purple-hemmed with blue lining in hood. No marks.

167

MC-10
MUNICH CHILD. Stoneware; ¼-liter, 6¾″ (17.1 cm); ½-liter, 8¼″ (21 cm). Similar to the prior Child, but shown in two sizes. Different thumb-lifts. No marks, only GESETZLICH GES-CHÜTZT.

MC-11
MUNICH CHILD. Stoneware; ¹⁄₁₆-liter, 4½″ (11.4 cm); ¼-liter, 6¾″ (17.1 cm); ½-liter, 8¼″ (21 cm). This set is shown in three sizes (⅛-liter missing). All steins similar.

MC-12

MUNICH CHILD. Porcelain; ⅛-liter, 5¾″ (14.6 cm); ¼-liter, 6¾″ (17.1 cm); ½-liter, 8″ (20.3 cm). All basically similar (*ECS-380*). Stein in right hand, a book (Bible?) in left hand with radishes under left arm. On the ½-liter steins, the stein held by Child is three-dimensional. Heavy pewter rim around lid. Variety of thumblifts, from plain to "twin towers." Robes and hoods either rust brown or black with yellow or rust lining; yellow scapular. Stein (with HB) in pastel colors; lid is gold or silver. Book either violet or blue; radishes vary from tan to brown, green leaves. Well-detailed lifelike faces with blonde hair. No marks. It is believed that these steins were manufactured over a long period of time, possibly even after World War II.

MC-13

MUNICH CHILD. ⅛-liter porcelain; 5¾″ (14.6 cm). Similar to *ECS-380*. Child holds a foaming HB stein (gold lid) in right hand, a beaker and two radishes in left. The glazed cherub-like face exhibits a very cheerful expression. No marks.

MC-14

MUNICH CHILD. 1-liter stoneware; 11″ (27.9 cm). A mate to the series depicted in *ECS*-388 and 399. Here the Child holds a HB stein and radishes in the right hand, roast chicken in the left. Relief and incised decorations. Bavarian Lion on shield, at bottom of scapular. *"Gruss aus München"* across belt. Very natural lifelike face. Well glazed. Marked Reinhold Merkelbach (5a) and moldmark # 564 impressed in bottom.

MC-15

MUNICH CHILD. 3/10-liter stoneware; 6¼″ (15.9 cm). Similar to *ECS*-388. This stein is part of a sized set (¼-, ⅓-, ½-, and 1-liter) made by Reinhold Merkelbach (5a). All are characterized by the roast chicken (i.e., one of the food "specialties" of the Munich Octoberfest).

MC-16

MUNICH CHILD. Stoneware; 1-liter, 11″ (27.9 cm); ½-liter 8″ (20.3 cm). Here the stein identified in the prior picture is seen together with the Child *ECS*-389. Stein and radishes in right hand, roast chicken in left. Well detailed face. Pewter-rimmed lid. Marked Reinhold Merkelbach (5a). 1-liter moldmark # 564; ½-liter moldmark #323.

MC-17

MUNICH CHILD. Stoneware; ³⁄₁₀-liter, 6¼″ (15.9 cm); ½-liter, 8″ (20.3 cm); 1-liter, 11″ (27.9 cm). Set of three RM steins all characterized by roast chicken being held in the left hand. All have different symbols shown on the bottom of the scapular (Bavarian rhombus crest; Church of Our Lady towers; Bavarian Lion). *"Gruss aus München"* appears across the wide belts. The ½-liter (middle) stein has a "pale face," the other two have realistically colored skin tones. Marked Reinhold Merkelbach (5a).

MC-18

MUNICH CHILD. ¼-liter porcelain; 6¾″ (17.1 cm). Similar to MC-21. However, the hood is not as pointed. On the bottom of the yellow scapular is *"Münch'ner Kindl"* on a blue field. The lid (head, shoulders) is set in a pewter ring. Heavy pewter fittings, well-detailed face. Lithophane of the Bavaria Statue in front of Ruhmeshalle. Similar to *ECS*-372, except the Child holds a beer stein and radishes, rather than the Bible. Marked Martin Pauson, München (14) along the rear, under the handle.

MC-19

MUNICH CHILD. ½-liter porcelain; 7¾″ (19.7 cm). Similar to the prior piece. Here the Child is holding a foaming stein and a bunch of radishes. *"Gruss aus München"* is written in old English script along the bottom on a blue background. The lithophane shows the Munich Hofbrauhaus garden. No marks.

MC-20
MUNICH CHILD. Porcelain. A multiple photo of three steins MC-18, 19, and 21. Notice the similarity in the scapulars with the tan borders.

MC-21
MUNICH CHILD. ½-liter porcelain; 7¾″ (19.7 cm). Holding open beer stein and single radish. Black robe with yellow hood lining. Yellow scapular with tan borders. Lithophane of Bavaria and Ruhmeshalle. No marks.

MC-22
MUNICH CHILD. ½-liter porcelain; 7¾″ (19.7 cm). This smiling Child holds a large crest of Bavaria in the right hand, a HB stein in the left. A three-dimensional depiction of the twin towers of the Frauenkirche at base. Black robe and hood, with orange scapular and cuffs. No marks.

MC-23

MUNICH CHILD. ¼-liter stoneware; 7¼″ (18.4 cm). This polychrome piece has a foaming grey stein in the right hand; red book (of law) in the left. Yellow/orange scapular. Face is similar to *ECS*-384, but no marks, only moldmark # 730 GESETZ-LICH GESCHÜTZT, GERMANY.

MC-24

MUNICH CHILD. ½-liter stoneware; 9½″ (24.1 cm). Very similar to *ECS*-394, except the Child is holding a Bible in its left hand instead of the usual radish. No marks, only the incised number 15 appears on the bottom. The sides of the base are straight in contrast to the flaring as seen on *ECS*-394. Identified as Marzi & Remy (9).

MC-25

MUNICH CHILD. ½-liter. *ECS*-394 (left) alongside the previously described Child.

MC-26
MUNICH CHILD. ¼-liter porcelain; 8¼″ (21 cm).
Similar to *ECS*-379. Polychrome; bisque lifelike
face. Child holds giant radishes in both hands.
Black robe and hood, gold lining. Gold scapular,
white sleeves, red shoes. Twin towers thumblift.
Lithophane of Bavaria in front of Ruhmeshalle.
Marked Jos. M. Mayer, München Bierkrugfabrik.
(12).

MC-27
Signature markings found on lower border, under
handle.

MC-28
MUNICH CHILD. ⅛-liter, 6″ (15.2 cm); ¼-liter,
8½″ (21.6 cm); ½-liter, 9½″ (24.1 cm). Similar
steins, described in the previous photograph. All
have identical lithophanes of Bavaria (proportional
to the size of the stein). Jos. M. Mayer, München
Bierkrugfabrik (12).

MC-29

MUNICH CHILD. ½-liter porcelain; 8¾" (22.2 cm). Similar to *ECS*-368. Child holds a large radish in the left hand, nothing in the right one. Bisque lifelike face, very realistic. "Church of Our Lady" twin-towered thumblift. Signed "Martin Pauson— München" on a white panel at rear base. It is doubtful whether Pauson was a manufacturer. The excellent quality lithophane shows the Hofbrauhaus beer garden in Munich.

MC-30

MUNICH CHILD. 1-liter earthenware; 11" (27.9 cm). Part of a series of greyish cream and black steins. Radish in the right hand, HB stein in the left. Beads hang from left wrist. *"München"* along the bottom front panel. No marks, only moldmark # 900.

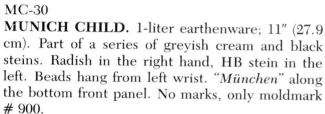

MC-31

MUNICH CHILD. ½-liter stoneware; 6¾" (17.1 cm). This happy Child holds a foaming stein with both hands. Under the right arm are two "Happy Radishes." Robe and pointed cowling are dark brown with light shadings. Accent in golden brown. Rust cuffs and base. No marks, only moldmark # 1569, GERMANY.

MC-32

MUNICH CHILD. ½-liter porcelain; 8½″ (21.6 cm). The figure shown holds a "tower" stein in the left hand, nothing in the right. Radishes are loosely dangling from the front. The black robe is covered with an amber shawl. A lithophane shows a man and woman in the woods. No marks.

MC-33

MUNICH CHILD. ½-liter earthenware; 10½″ (26.7 cm). This glazed *kindl* holds a foamy stein in the left hand, radishes in the right. The primitive face resembles the Monk (*ECS*-352). Unusual "modern art" appearance. The poor glaze is generally a matte appearance. Ca. 1930. Marked Gilles & Sohn (32a).

MC-34

MUNICH CHILD. ½-liter stoneware; 9″ (22.9 cm). Holding a radish in the right hand and a silver-lidded open stein in the left. Black robe and cowling, with red "hem" at base. Yellow/orange scapular and cuffs. No marks. Also made in ¼-liter size moldmarked # 1197.

MC-35
MUNICH CHILD. ½-liter stoneware; 8″ (20.3 cm). Similar to Reinemann-type. Black robe and hood, yellow lining, yellow scapular, red arm sleeves. Lifelike features. An old stein, good quality. No marks. (ca. 1910).

MC-36
MUNICH CHILD. ¼-liter stoneware; 7″ (17.8 cm). An unusual *Muenchen Kindl* in that the Child is not wearing the usual hood, but a small cap. The cream collar and necklace are more associated with nobility. A plaque reading *"Gruss aus München"* with the twin towers on the front near the base. Another version of this stein shows the kindl wearing a skull-type cap. Marked JOSEF M. MAYER, MÜNCHEN (12), GESETZLICH GESCHÜTZT.

MC-37
MUNICH CHILD. ¼-liter stoneware; 7½″ (19.1 cm). Similar to *ECS-370* and the larger *ECS-387*. The shield held by the Child shows only the twin domes of the Frauenkirche Church. A rear banner reads *"Prosit."* No marks, only the moldmark # 895. Identified as Reinhold Merkelbach (5).

MC-38
MUNICH CHILD. ¼-liter salt-glaze stoneware; 5″ (12.7 cm). A blue/grey Child, holding a stein in the right hand (marked *"HB—Gruss aus München"*). Radishes in the left hand, others under left arm. Well-detailed face, good relief work. Cobalt-blue, with face, scapular, stein, and radishes in grey. No marks, only the moldmark # 117G (incised). Most likely turn of the century, Westerwald area.

MC-39
MUNICH CHILD. ½-liter stoneware; 9½″ (24.1 cm). This polychrome figurine holds a tall open stein in the right hand, radishes with long hanging green leaves in the left. Black robe and hood, yellow scapular edged in brown. A brown "hem" on robe. Face and hands have very lifelike coloration. Incised MUSTERSCHUTZ (10d) and Thewalt (7a), moldmark # 184. Recently reproduced by Thewalt. See "Contemporary Steins" # 9002.

MC-40
MUNICH CHILD. 1-liter stoneware; 12″ (30.5 cm). Similar to *ECS*-382. This tall polychrome figurine has the usual pose typical of the many steins depicted in this section. An HB stein in the right hand, two radishes in the left. *"Gruss aus"* is written across top of scapular, the *"München"* across the bottom. Marked with mark similar to that found on *ECS*-391 (37).

MC-41

MUNICH CHILD. ¼-liter stoneware; 6½" (16.5 cm). This smiling piece has three radishes and an HB stein. No marks, only the moldmark # 1380 GERMANY. Also made in a 1-liter size mold-marked # 1650.

MC-42

MUNICH CHILD. ½-liter stoneware; 8" (20.3 cm). Similar to *ECS*-392 and 393. The difference is that this stein is ½-liter, with a different face. The body is a typical ½-liter HB (Hofbrau) stein with arms. The left holds four foaming steins, the right holds several radishes. Pewter-rimmed lid is the head, smiling face covered with a pointed hood. Filigreed pewter thumbrest. The robe is cobalt-blue with red linings; the body is grey. Skintones are very natural, with rosy cheeks. No marks, only moldmark # 1585, GERMANY. *ECS*-393 and 392 were identified as Steinzeugwerke (23). This stein was made by the same manufacturer.

MC-43

MUNICH CHILD. 1-liter stoneware; 10½" (26.7 cm). Same as prior stein, however, in the larger 1-liter size. No marks, only moldmark # 1285. Possibly Steinzeugwerke (23).

MC-44

MC-46

MC-44
MUNICH CHILD. ⅛-liter porcelain; 6″ (15.2 cm). Holds an open grey stein in the right hand, radishes in the left. Black robe and hood, gold lining. No marks.

MC-45
MUNICH CHILD. ⅛-liter porcelain; 4½″ (11.4 cm). A miniature version of *ECS*-369. Black robe and pointed cowl. Light blue linings of hood and cuffs. The Child holds a single radish in the left hand, nothing in the right. The lithophane shows a street scene. Once again it is signed "Martin Pauson—München" on a white panel, under the handle.

MC-46
MUNICH CHILD. ¹⁄₁₆-liter porcelain; 3″ (7.6 cm). This miniature holds a Bible in the right hand, radishes in the other. No marks.

MC-47
MUNICH CHILD. ⅛-liter stoneware; 5½″ (14 cm). Holding law book in the right hand, radishes in the left. Pewter hinge attached directly to lid (head) with rivet. Good relief work. Cream, blue, and green with black robe and hood. No marks, only moldmark # 1267. Manufactured ca. 1900.

MC-45

MC-47

MC-48
MUNICH CHILD. 1/16-liter pewter; 3¼″ (8.3 cm).
A tiny Child, holding a very large stein in the right
hand, radishes in the left. No marks.

MC-49
MUNICH CHILD. 1/16-liter pewter; 4½″ (11.4 cm).
Holding a pewter tankard with HB in the right
hand, radishes in the left. Good relief work. All
pewter with integrally cast hinge-post. Pewter is
well finished inside and out. No marks.

Pewter goes back to ancient times. It was an invention of the Bronze Age metalworkers who discovered that tin—a shiny, brittle metal—could be
rendered both more malleable and more durable
when alloyed with other metals. The first pewter
was a copper-tin alloy, and objects made of it have
been found in excavations in China, Egypt, and
Roman-occupied Britain. But the most widely used
ingredient until the last century was lead, which
gives pewter its heft. From whatever age, the pewter is apt to be tin alloyed in varying proportions
with lead, copper, bismuth, or antimony.

MC-50
MUNICH CHILD. 1/8-liter stoneware; 5¼″ (13.3
cm). Nicely detailed, good relief work. Lid is set in
pewter ring; filigreed thumbrest. Child holds HB
stein and radishes. Red cowl-lining; yellow scapular, bottom rim outlined in gold. Manufactured
early 1900s. No marks, only moldmark # 298.

MC-51
MUNICH CHILD. 1/8-liter stoneware; 5¼″ (13.3
cm). Similar to prior stein. The steins are basically
identical except that the one on the left has better
detail. Child on the right has inferior detail, twin-
towers thumblift, plain base. No marks, only moldmark # 298.

MUNICH CHILD. ½-liter salt-glaze stoneware. Similar to the next stein in coloring. Here the Child holds a grey HB foaming stein in the right hand, radishes in the left. Blue, with face, inside of hood, scapular, stein, and radishes kept grey. No marks, only the moldmark # 298. Most likely from the Hoehr-Grenzhausen (Westerwald) area. Ca. 1900.

MC-53

MUNICH CHILD. ⅓-liter salt-glaze stoneware; 4″ (10.2 cm). A very small blue/grey Child holding a stein saying *"Gruss aus München* HB" in the right hand, radishes in the left. Marked JGN.

MC-54

MUNICH CHILD. ½-liter stoneware; 8½″ (21.6 cm). Similar to *ECS-391*. Possible mate to MC-40. Marked with the same marking and the impressed moldmark # 117,(37).

SK-1

SKULL. ½-liter porcelain; 5″ (12.7 cm). This bisque piece has a very unusual handle in the shape of a red devil. The thumblift's band eminates from the devil's waist and extends over its head to attach to the pewter lid. No marks. Dated 1878 (under the handle).

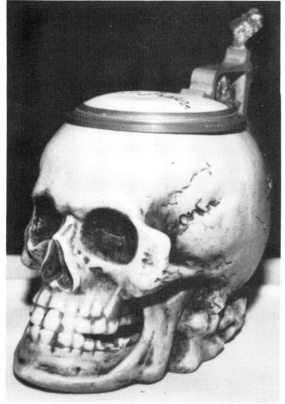

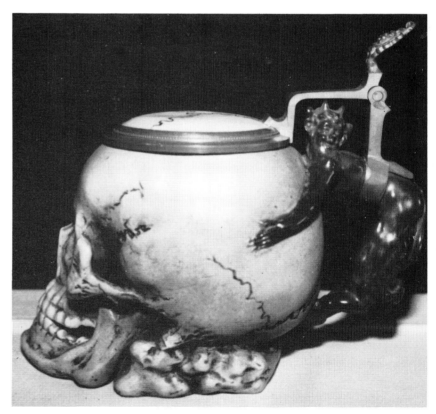

SK-2, 3

SKULL. ½-liter porcelain; 5″ (12.7 cm). Similar to the previous skull, except for the lid insert, which is constructed of the same bisque material. No marks. Dated 1878 (under the handle).

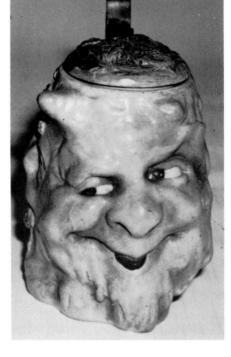

SK-4

SKULL. ½-liter stoneware; 7″ (17.8 cm). This plain brownish grey stein is missing several teeth. No marks, only GESETZLICH GESCHÜTZT. Identified as Steinzeugwerke (23). See "Old Catalogs."

SK-5

SATAN. ½-liter stoneware; 6½″ (16.5 cm). Same stein as *ECS-414*, except with the original stoneware lid. Marked Merkelbach & Wick (4b) and # 2601.

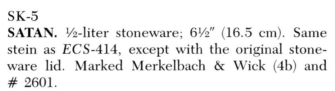

SK-6

SATAN. ½-liter stoneware; 8″ (20.3 cm). A highly glazed comical rendition of another sinister devil. The front panel reads: "*Wer mit mir schliesst einen Packt, dem bleibt der Magen stets intakt.*" (Whoever signs a pact with me, From hunger will forever be free.) No marks, only the moldmark # 1565, GERMANY. Identified as Steinzeugwerke (23). See "Old Catalogs."

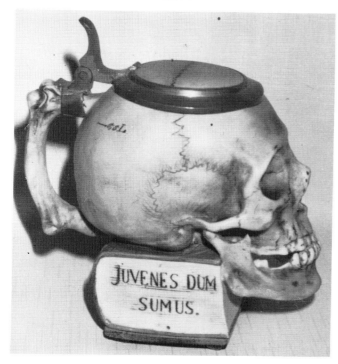

SK-8

SKULL. ½-liter porcelain, 5½″ (14 cm). *ECS-400* shown with a very unusual eagle thumblift. This piece is marked Ernst Bohne (2c).

SK-9, 10

SKULL ON BOOK. ½-liter porcelain; 5½″ (14 cm). Similar to other bisque steins depicting skulls. The book is inscribed with the Latin *"Gaudeamus igitur, juvenes dum sumus."* (Let us therefore rejoice while we are still young.) See *ECS-400* and *ECS-9* for further explanations. Marked Schierholz & Söhn (1b).

SKULL ON BOOK. ½-liter porcelain; 7″ (17.8 cm). Similar to *ECS-400*, except this bisque head sits atop a much larger *Commersbuch* book (provisions for a music box). The book is once again inscribed with the Latin *"Gaudeamus Igitur, Juvenes dum sumus."* (Let us therefore rejoice while we are still young.) No marks. Identified as Ernst Bohne (2).

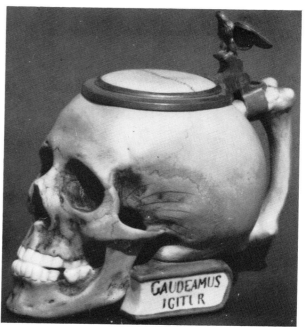

SK-8

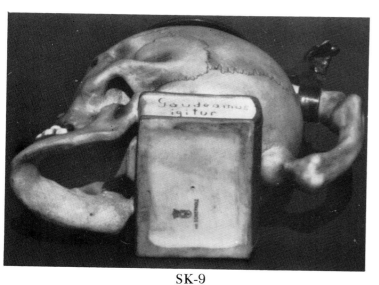

SK-9

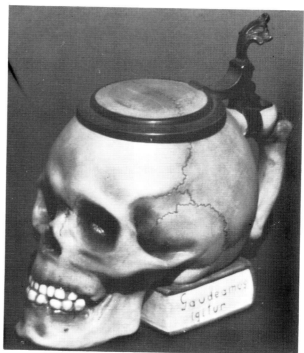

SK-10

SK-11
SKULL. ¼-liter porcelain; 3½" (8.9 cm). Another bisque version. Much smaller than most of the others. No marks. Probably made by Ernst Bohne (2).

SK-12
SKULL. ½-liter stoneware; 8" (20.3 cm). This plain, glossy piece, marked # 1796, GESETZ-LICH GESCHÜTZT GERMANY has been identified as Marzi & Remy (9). See "Old Catalogs."

SK-13
SKULL. ¹⁄₁₆-liter porcelain; 2¾" (7 cm). Similar to the prior ¼-liter skull. Here it appears alongside the ½-liter size. No marks.

It was also produced in the ⁴⁄₁₀-liter size. Probably made by Ernst Bohne (2). This ½-liter version is the one most often used on the skull regimental steins (see *ECS-406*). It was also made in stoneware.

ᛏᚢowers

TO-1

NUREMBERG TOWERS. ½-liter stoneware; 9½″ (24.1 cm). Two variations of the Tower as described in *ECS*-416. The 4F stein (right) reads: "*X DEUTSCHES TURNFEST, NÜRNBERG,*" (10th German Turnfest, Nuremberg.) Marked F&M/N (22), L. Ostermayr, Nürnberg, moldmark # 1190, GESETZLICH GESCHÜTZT. Occasionally seen marked Georg Leykauf, Nürnberg (a store in Nuremberg). It should be noted that L. Ostermayr was the distributor, not the manufacturer.

The tower on the left shows scenes of Nuremberg. Sometimes seen with a rear panel that reads: "*Gruss aus Nürnberg,*" (Greetings from Nuremberg). Please see "The Towers of Nuremberg" by Art Maethner, *Prosit* (no. 34, January 1974).

TO-2

NUREMBERG TOWER. ½-liter stoneware; 9½″ (24.1 cm). The Father Jahn panel shows his profile with the inscription "*18–22 Juli 1903, Vater Jahn.*" The left stein shows scenes of Nuremberg. Marked F&M/N (22), moldmark # 1190, GESETZLICH GESCHÜTZT.

TO-3

NUREMBERG TOWER. ⅛-liter stoneware; 6″ (15.2 cm). A similar smaller version of *ECS-416*. This beige and blue tower is etched with two circular scenes on the side. One shows the city of Nuremberg, the other panel shows a relief of Hans Sachs, famous Meistersinger. A matching roof forms the lid.

Two lines of verse are incised in the ribbons below the panels "*27 31 JULI NÜRNBERG 1912*" and "*VIII DEUTSCHES SÄNGERBUNDE FEST*" (27–31 July Nuremberg 1912, 8th German song group festival). "*Gruss aus Nürnberg*" (Greetings from Nuremberg) appear under the handle. Marked F&M/N (22), moldmark # 520. Also made in a ½-liter version (similar to TO-1).

TO-4

NUREMBERG TOWER. ⅛-liter stoneware; 6″ (15.2 cm). This beige/cream piece has an inscription below the handle reading: "*Gruss aus Nürnberg.*" Similar to TO-3, but without the side panels. No marks, only moldmark # 6183.

TO-5   TO-6

TO-5, 6

TOWER. ½-liter stoneware; 10¼″ (26 cm). A stylized Nuremberg Tower, similar to the previously described versions. However, here we see green and brown vines crawling the cream/beige brickwork. The unique thumblift depicts a small helmeted young man holding two shields. This stein was also manufactured in blue/grey stoneware. No marks, only moldmark # 972. Note entrance in rear of stein.

NUREMBERG TOWER. This tower is one of the four great round tower gates (formerly called the Spittlertorturm or Spittler Gate Tower) within the walls of old Nuremberg.

TO-8

NUREMBERG TOWER. 2½-liter stoneware; 16½″ (41.9 cm). A very large Nuremberg tower. This blue/grey piece is adorned with a pewter lid-roof, topped with a weather vane. The crest of Nuremberg is shown in the oversized thumblift. The front panel also shows the crest of Nuremberg. Marked T.W. (20a), GESETZLICH GESCHÜTZT.

TO-9

NUREMBERG TOWERS. 1-liter stoneware; 10¾″ (27.3 cm); ½-liter, 8″ (20.3 cm). Two size variations of the same stein. Marked T.W. (20a).

TO-10

NUREMBERG TOWERS. ½-liter stoneware; 8″ (20.3 cm); ⅛-liter, 5″ (12.7 cm). The larger piece is marked T.W. (20), while the smaller has the HR (21a) markings (see "HR Steins," Wald, p. 29). This stein also was made with no markings on the base.

TO-11

EAST BERLIN TOWN HALL. ½-liter porcelain; 10½″ (26.7 cm). Similar to the Tower *ECS-427*, however, this piece is adorned by the correct turret-type lid. The bisque is decorated with fine detail in the bricks, windows, and clocks. The Town Hall, built in 1868, stands on Alexander Platz. The lithophane shows two men and a woman sitting around a tavern table. No marks.

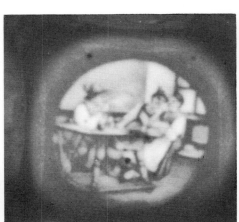

TO-13
LITHOPHANE.

TO-12
EAST BERLIN TOWN HALL.

TO-14
NUREMBERG TOWER. ½-liter stoneware; 9″ (22.9 cm). Another deeply incised blue-bricked tower. The pewter thumblift has a similar young lad holding two shields of Nuremberg. No marks, only the moldmark # 972.

TO-15
FRAUENKIRCHE TOWER. ¼-liter stoneware; 5¾″ (14.6 cm). A miniature version of *ECS-419*. There are some minor differences, notice the smaller upper windows and the clocks reading two o'clock. The blue/grey stein is topped with a pewter onion dome lid. No marks, only MADE IN GERMANY.

TO-16
NUREMBERG TOWER. ⅛-liter pewter; 4½″ (11.4 cm). A miniature pewter variation of the many Nuremberg towers seen in this section. No marks, only Gesetzl. Geschützt.

TO-17

TOWER. 1-liter pewter; 16″ (40.6 cm). Similar to *ECS-424*, this stein shows twin-turreted balconies, with three windows. An arch is shown over the doorway. Some copper and brass metal is used on the various windows and turrets. No marks.

TO-18

TOWER. ½-liter pewter; 12″ (30.5 cm). A smaller version of *ECS-424*. The front balcony is smaller, and a figure is not present on the top parapet. Some copper and brass is also present on windows and turrets. No marks.

TO-19

TOWER. 1-liter pewter; 13½″ (34.3 cm). A very unusual crude handmade pewter piece. Along the front surface is seen a three-dimensional figure of an old man. He leans out of the open window, waving a beer stein. Bricks are "etched" into the body of the base. The lid consists of the turret. A very difficult to read mark is struck into the bottom.

WA-1

FISH. ½-liter porcelain; 8″ (20.3 cm). Four fish are standing on their tails. An additional fish head appears out of the middle of the group. The handle also is formed by a fish. Marked Musterschutz (10a) and the crosshatch mark (1a).*

WA-2

FROG. ½-liter stoneware; 6½″ (16.5 cm). Two variations of *ECS-438*. The "natural" green on the left, cream-colored on the right. No marks, only moldmark # 1429, GERMANY.

*Made by Schierholz and Sohn.

WA-3
FROG ON BOOK. ½-liter porcelain; 9½″ (24.1 cm). Similar to *ECS-435*, except sitting on a book (ala "Skull on Book"). The base is hollow to house a music box. No marks. Probably made by Ernst Bohne.

WA-4
FROG. (*ECS-435*) alongside FROG ON BOOK.

Frogs were depicted on many pieces (see *ECS 432–439*). Many steins and mugs were made with stoneware or porcelain frogs in the bottom (see below). The frog was hidden beneath the full stein, but would seem to rise out of the beer as the stein was emptied. It was a favorite trick to give a stein with a frog in the bottom to your loved one after she had had a few, and then watch her reaction as the frog appeared. There was many a scream and many a broken stein as it was flung against the wall.

WA-5
A little humor is quite often found lurking in the bottom of the stein. Here a smiling green frog leers back as the drinker empties his beer.

ℳiscellaneous

MI-1
BEEHIVES. ½-liter stoneware; 7¼″ (18.4 cm). Two variations of *ECS*-454. Left shows seventeen bees flitting around. The older version to the right has twenty bees. Marked Reinhold Merkelbach (5a), moldmark # 1384. See "Old Catalogs."

MI-2, 3
ARMORED KNIGHT. ½-liter stoneware; 8½″ (21.6 cm). Similar to *ECS*-462, however, in full color. Notice the unique handle. Marked F&M/N (22) and MUSTERSCHUTZ.

MI-4

FRANCO-PRUSSIAN TANKARD. ½-liter pewter; 8″ (20.3 cm). A very ornate figural lid, depicting two Schlitt-like men fighting. It is supposedly Emperor Napoleon III (above the handle) in a soft floppy hat trying to wrest away the sleeping place (as signified by the puffy pillow on the front of the lid) of the German "Michel" (a self-descriptive term by Germans for Germany, similar to the American "Yankee"). The stein alludes to the happenings of the Franco-Prussian War of 1870/71 in which Prussia defeated France. We thank Lotti Lopez for this version of the stein. Another story as related by Art Maethner tells of the sleeping Michel, totally oblivious to that which was occurring around him. The phrase *Ich will meine Ruhe Haben* (I want to be left in peace, or alone), stems from this period. This scene shows him being rudely awakened by an officer who is trying to conscript him into the army. However, Michel is not about to give in without a fight. Marked F. Barth, München 1871. Refers to Ferdinand Barth, a designer for J. Lichtinger.

MI-5

FRANZ LISZT. ½-liter porcelain; 7″ (17.8 cm). Not a true character stein, but interesting enough to show. The head of Hungarian composer, Liszt (1811–86), forms the lid finial. No marks.

MI-6

FOAMING STEIN. 1-liter stoneware; 10″ (25.4 cm). The base is a deep brown mug ringed by a white foamy beer. The pewter lid is topped by an open-mouthed man, forming the thumblift. No marks.

MI-7

INNKEEPER. ½-liter porcelain; 8½″ (21.6 cm). This egg-shaped stein shows a smiling, nightcapped innkeeper *(Gastwirt)* pointing to the many marks on the slate, reminding his guest that perhaps he has had more than enough to drink. Innkeepers, particularly in the Rhineland, often wore such caps as part of their everyday dress. The Monkey handle would also account for the symbol for the omnipresent state of inebriation. Green, leafy base. Marked Schierholz & Söhn (1b), moldmark # 129 10.

MI-8

KEG. ½-liter stoneware; 5″ (12.7 cm). Another stein in the shape of a brown beer barrel. This one's banner reads: *"Wohl bekomm's!"* (To your health!) No marks, only moldmark, # 1058, GERMANY. Made by J. W. Remy (39). This stein also appears in a cream coloration. This version was also made with a man coming out of the top of the keg. Very similar to Rosskopf & Gerz # 609 (38). See "Old Catalogs."

MI-9

GLOBE. ½-liter stoneware; 8″ (20.3 cm). A sphere-shape representation of the earth. The green and pink continents are incised into the blue oceans. A finial of Dr. Frederick Albert Cook (1865–1940) holding an American flag stands atop the lid. Cook, an American explorer, claimed to have discovered the North Pole in September 1908. A similar stein was manufactured with a finial of Admiral Robert Peary (1856–1920). The U.S. Congress and most geographical institutions accept Peary's claim as the more valid one. The Peary finial shows him cradling a flag in his left arm; a husky sits by his feet. The relief continents and seas are labeled in English. The Peary stein, identified as Steinzeugwerke (23), moldmark # 2368a (see "Old Catalogs") lacks the longitudinal and latitudinal marks seen on this piece. This piece has also been seen with no finial present. Marked GERMANY, moldmark # 2368.

MI-10

ELF. 1-liter stoneware; 10″ (25.4 cm). A hooded dwarf-like head appears above the base of this barrel-shaped stein. Three beige elves frolic through a colorful grape-picking scene. The upper green band reads: "ES LEBE WAS AUF ERDEN HIER" the lower "SICH LABEN MACH AN WEIN UND BIER," (Something on earth is living here which refreshes itself on wine and beer.) The handle is formed by the vineyard branches. Marked # 97 Thewalt (7c), GERMANY.

MI-11

LANTERN. ½-liter stoneware; 7″ (17.8 cm). This grey and black piece resembles an antique lantern. The pewter lid is adorned with a ring handle finial. No marks.

MI-12

LANTERN. ⁴⁄₁₀-liter glass; 7½″ (19.1 cm). Similar to the prior stein. The pewter lid does not attach to the handle, but to a special attachment located just above the glass handle. Colors are black, gold, and clear glass. No marks, only the relief lettering GES. GESCH, which can be seen when peering into the stein.

MI-13

BARREL. ½-liter stoneware; 8″ (20.3 cm). Constructed in the shape, coloring, and appearance of a wooden-staved barrel. Lid has an insert with two brown monkeys, each holding beige drinking vessels and sitting on green grass. Gold-lustre straps circumvent the body. The indented center panel has a scene with the appliqued figure of an inebriated man holding onto the wall of a building. Behind the man is a street, with a scene of the front of the building with two windows and a door. The body has two incised dark brown panels with raised lettering: *"Kommst du aus der Kneipe raus,"* and *"Bringst einen Affen mit nach Haus."* (When from the inn you choose to roam, You'll bring your drunken state back home.) No marks, only moldmark # 1598, GERMANY. Possibly Steinzeugwerke (23).

MI-14

BASKETWEAVE. ¾-liter stoneware; 7½″ (19.1 cm). This beige and cream stein, with green trim, has the appearance of a woven basket. The scroll reads: *"Trinken ist immer gesund."* (Drinking is always healthy.) No marks, only the moldmark # 977, GERMANY.

MI-15

TAXES TANKARD. ¼–½-liter porcelain; 4¾″ (12.1 cm). This comical stein should be used after April 15th. The wording *"Steuern"* and *"Seidel"* (Taxes tankard) are written across the front. The vessel seems to contain ½ liter, but in fact, holds only ¼ liter. The two vessels depicted on the face of the stein bear this out. The word *Sonst* means the usual, or the norm while the word *Jetzt* means now, or the present condition. A full stein of beer and a half-full glass is shown. The side panel shows a picture of von Bülow (the Minister of Finance). The unusual part of the piece is that the outside is the size of a ½-liter stein. When opened, the drinking vessel measures only ¼ liter! Things were rough even in 1909. No marks. Probably Ernst Bohne.

MI-16

BEAR. ½-liter stoneware; 8¾″ (22.2 cm). The blue-grey and brown body shows several panels of cats. The upper band reads: *"Es ist besser mit Affen mit Kater und Bären."* (Your precious time is better spent with tomcat, ape and bear.) The lower reads: *"Als allzeit mit Ochsen und Eseln zu verkehren."* (The stubborn ox and foolish bear let other folks repent.)

A crouched bear forms the handle. Atop the lid sits a bear-like cat holding a boot that represents a large tankard. No marks, only the moldmark, # 940 15, GESETZLICH GESCHÜTZT.

Note: The word *Bear* has the figurative meaning of an uncouth fellow, while the phrase *einen Affen haben* refers to someone in a state of intoxication. The word *Kater* refers to a severe hangover. The word *Ochse* has the figurative meaning of a "blockhead," while the word *Esel* means figuratively "a silly ass" or a "fool."

(Credit to Art Maethner)

MI-17

DWARF. ½-liter parian; 7¾″ (19.7 cm). Grey figures are seen in relief around the base. A kneeling dwarf is atop the stoneware lid insert. No marks, only the incised # 485. Identified as Villeroy & Boch (16). Manufactured in mid-1850s.

MI-18

STAG. ³⁄₁₀-liter bisque porcelain; 4¼″ (11.4 cm). Though not true character steins, this pair would show beautifully in any collection. The Bison, *ECS-74*, on the right. No marks.

MI-20

MI-19

MI-19, 20

MOUNTAIN. 1-liter stoneware; 9½″ (24.1 cm).
Another variation of the "Zugspitze" (*ECS-444*).
This piece shows a different mountain. Along the
side can be seen a mountain climber behind a rock.
A colorful chalet is near the top. The stoneware lid
is topped by a church finial (missing the cross in
this piece). The interesting handle is formed by a
fire-breathing dragon. The word "*TAZLWURM*"
(Tazl Dragon) appears below the handle. The words
"*NACH BIRKENSTEIN*" (to Birkenstein) are in-
cised around the base. Also "*NACH BRANEN-
BURG*" (to Branenburg) and "*NACH BAIRISCH
ZELL*" (to Bairisch Zel) are etched into two rocks.
These three signs are in reference to three small
towns in southern Bavaria on the Bavarian-Austrian
Alpine border. The base is lined with a row of edel-
weis. The pewter thumblift depicts a young moun-
taineer. No marks, only the incised GESETZLICH
GESCHÜTZT.

MI-21

ZUGSPITZE. ½-liter stoneware; 8″ (20.3 cm).
Same as *ECS-444*. Marked MARTIN PAUSON
MÜNCHEN (14a).

MI-22
CHRISTOPHER COLUMBUS. ½-liter stoneware; 6¼″ (15.9 cm). A blue/grey salt-glazed stein in the likeness of an egg. The story goes: *"Das Ei des Kolumbus."* It seems that after Columbus discovered America, Cardinal Mendoza held a big banquet in his honor and highly praised him. There were, however, many men present who did not like Columbus, especially since his father was an Italian. They said, "any sailor who sails upon the seas to the west could discover the New World," and mocked him saying: *"Was Kolumbus kann, können wir auch!"* (What Columbus can, can we also!) Columbus heard all this, took an egg, and asked the gentlemen if they could make it stand on end. One after another tried, but failed. So they all said, even Columbus can't do this. Columbus then took the egg and set it down a little hard, slightly crushing the bottom of the shell, so it stood perfectly on end. Then with a smile on his face Columbus echoed the words of the gentlemen: "What Columbus can, can we also." The gentlemen then, of course, understood that it was not the doing, but the knowing how to do, that made him a great man.

The three bas-relief panels show the ship, the Santa Maria; a bust of Christoph(er) Columbus and a globe of the western hemisphere. The stoneware lid shows an anchor with twining vines. It may have been manufactured for the Columbian Exposition of 1893. Marked RH (18a) GERMANY. It also was made in cream and green coloring. See "Old Catalogs." Reinhold Hanke # 1150.

MI-23
PINECONE. ¾-liter stoneware; 10¼″ (26 cm). Scene of several dogs chasing an elk. The upper blue band reads: *"HATZ UND GEJAGD IS EDEL FREYD."* (The hunter's chase is never base.) No marks. Only GERMANY. Identified as J. W. Remy (39). See "Old Catalogs," # 976.

MI-24
LADY WITH NIGHTCAP. 1-liter stoneware; 10¼″ (26 cm). This lovely smiling *HAUSFRAU* is wearing a blue ruffled nightcap tied with a yellow bow under her chin. Her plump face surrounded by brown hair, has blue eyes and very red lips. No marks, only moldmark # 645.

MI-25
MAN WITH PIPE. 1-liter stoneware; 12″ (30.5 cm). A mate to the prior stein. The face of a man with half-closed eyes. Smoke lazily ascends from his pipe. His blue fez-like night cap has a red tassel dangling down the side. No marks, only moldmark # 633.

MI-26
COFFEE POT. ½-liter enameled metal; 7½″ (19.1 cm). In the shape, and of the same metal, as an old-time coffee pot. Pewter lid with white porcelain insert. No marks.

MI-27
MONKEY CONTEMPLATING HIS ANCESTRY. ½-liter stoneware; 7½″ (19.1 cm). A comical reversal of the monkey pondering his descendants. The three-paneled off-white and green stein depicts (in the first panel) a monkey concentrating on a book of Homo Sapiens. The second panel shows him studying several Darwinian volumes of *Origin of the Species.* The last shows a spectacled primate peering at a skull. Below the panels is the Latin saying: "Quod Erat Demonstrandum" (Q.E.D.—Which was to be proved—geometry). The handle consists of another monkey biting the upper band. Could this stein be a monkey pondering whether man is *his* ancestor? No marks, only the moldmark # 1257, GERMANY. Identified as STEINZEUG-WERKE (23). See "Old Catalogs."

MI-29

MI-28, 29
Similar to the prior stein, but with lifelike colored monkeys. Same markings.

MI-28

MI-30
STAG HORN. ½-liter porcelain; 8″ (20.3 cm). This brown antler-like piece shows a pinkish-white boar in relief along the front surface. Handle is formed by another antler. Marked Musterschutz (10c).*

*Made by Schierholz and Sohn.

MI-31

TREE STUMP. ½-liter stoneware; 10¼″ (26 cm). This beige and brown stump is entwined with colorful vines and leaves (often with silver-colored leaves and vines). Handle formed by a limb. Pewter-rimmed lid, stoneware inlay with two leaves and a twig. Marked with the old Villeroy & Boch "Chewing gum mark," (16c) moldmark # 376.

MI-33

TREE STUMP. 1½-liter stoneware; 13½″ (34.3 cm). Another blue/grey depiction of a larger tree, the stump is covered with similarly colored flowers, leaves, and branches. Marked Merkelbach & Wick (4a).

MI-32

STAG HORN. ½-liter porcelain; 8″ (20.3 cm) to top of finial. A unique brownish piece. The beige front oval panel depicts four white deer. The pewter-rimmed lid is inset with a sitting hunter, his lazy dog sprawled between his legs. Handle is in the shape of an antler. No marks.

TREE STUMP. ½-liter stoneware; 5″ (12.7 cm). Again we see another variation of a tree-like stein. The beige/brown bark is surrounded with green leaves and brown branches. Handle is also in the shape of a branch. No marks.

MI-35

TREE STUMP. ½-liter stoneware; 6″ (15.2 cm). Shaped in the form of a stump, this ornate piece has a lid with another stump stein of the same decor, and theoretically, ad infinitum. Decorations are branches, oak leaves, and acorns. No marks.

Contemporary

FIRST, WE MUST DEFINE THE TERM "CONTEMPORARY" AND EXPLAIN HOW WE BASED OUR selection for the steins found in this chapter. We have chosen World War II as the dividing line in our definition of "old" and "contemporary" steins. This time frame seems to be the standard used amongst collectors today. Thus, any stein manufactured after World War II will be considered "contemporary" and fall into this chapter. We felt that by including these steins in a separate chapter rather than breaking them down into their respective categories, it will be easier for the reader to determine whether a stein is "old" or "contemporary."

While in most cases we can be fairly accurate in the selection of steins for this section, there is a small area of uncertainty that exists with certain steins. One of these grey areas concerns steins made by Eckhardt & Engler. We have included many of them here because they carry the base inscription, "Made in Western Germany." This, of course, would date them as post-war. However, some of these same pieces are only marked "Made in Germany." This leads us to believe that they could have been made prior to World War II. The quality of these two versions are identical in some cases, so we believe that they were produced both prior to and after the war. In fact, these same steins have been produced as early as 1917 by this factory. Therefore, a number of these steins could be shown in the regular categories of this catalog, but because most do say "Western Germany," we chose to show them only in this section so as not to confuse the reader. Regardless of when they were made, the quality of each individual piece is the main factor in collecting them.

Another confusing factor here is the appearance of the same stein with different factory marks and shown under more than one factory heading. This is a result of the buying and selling or interchanging of master molds or designs between various makers, especially in the Hoehr-Grenzhausen area. Since the major market after the war was here in the United States, whichever factory made a good contact in the United States would be the supplier of particular designs. This is one reason that many steins do not carry a factory mark.

In the past decade, Rastal-Werk has been a major distributor of character steins found here in the United States. They have acted as the main United States distributor of most of the character steins made by Matthias Girmscheid of recent date. To further confuse the issue, Rastal stamped their own name onto these stein bases. Since Girmscheid never did mark these pieces, we incorrectly assumed that Rastal was the manufacturer. In actuality, Rastal did not make any of the character steins attributed to them directly. They did copy some successful older steins and had them made exclusively for them by smaller, unknown workshops.

A larger number of the steins featured in this chapter are copies of familiar character steins made many years earlier. There seems to be very little in the way of totally new character designs. The quality of some of the newer copies is quite good. In fact, some are so well done that, if the marks were removed, they could easily be passed off as old steins to the unknowledgeable collector. The R.P.M. Drunken Monkey almost rivals the Musterschutz version. The Munich Tower stein by Rastal is almost identical to its T.W. counterpart.

In conclusion, we feel that age should not be the determining factor in our collecting of character steins. The main criteria should be quality and desirability. Remember, the contemporary steins of today are the antiques of tomorrow.

Ceramarte Ltd.

CO-1, 2

SCHULTZ, DOOLEY, OFFICER SUDDS, and the COUNTESS. In 1959 when television sets were giant pieces of furniture, TV viewers were introduced to a couple of mugs named Schultz and Dooley. Schultz, tall and mustachioed, spoke with a German accent, while the mild-mannered, pint-sized Dooley conversed in a gentle Irish brogue. Over the next half dozen years, along with their colorful sidekicks, Officer Suds and the Countess, they encountered a series of entertaining predicaments.

SCHULTZ. 1-liter stoneware; 11¼″ (28.6 cm). Ornately colored in dark blue, light blue, and gold.

DOOLEY. ½-liter stoneware; 6½″ (16.5 cm). Beige with red "hair," sports a bright green shamrock.

OFFICER SUDDS. ½-liter stoneware; 8½″ (21.6 cm). The fearless keeper of law and order. Is fitted in a handsome blue uniform and a black hat that forms the lid. Trimmed with gold buttons and badges.

COUNTESS. ½-liter stoneware; 7¼″ (18.4 cm). Is the most colorful of the group, from her bright floral design to her brilliant red hat and dried flower. Designed, of course, to catch Dooley's eye!

The steins were originally made for a promotion of the West End Brewing Company (WEBCO) of Utica, N.Y. by the firm of Wuerfel & Mueller; in recent years they have been produced in Brazil by Ceramarte Ltd. (28). Rio Negrinho, SC. Marked WEBCO and C within a circle. They are now being made by Simon Peter Gerz (8).

CO-3

FARMER MUGEE. ½-liter stoneware; 8½″ (21.6 cm). A recent addition to the above-mentioned group. All the above steins are now being produced in the Westerwald area of West Germany.

CO-4

WILLY BRANDT. ½-liter ceramic; 5¾″ (14.6 cm) to top of thumblift. A grey characterization of the former chancellor of West Germany. Black lettering on the rear reads: *"Lieber Kleine Schritte, als Grosse Sprünge."* (Better small steps than large leaps.) Marked Celtic.

CO-4

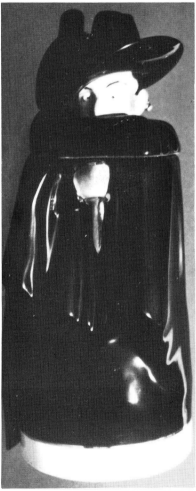

CO-5

SPY. ½-liter porcelain; 9¾″ (24.8 cm). This black agent of mystery carries a golden dagger. His skin-toned face peeks out of the black cape. A music box in the base plays a tune from "Dragnet." Sergeant Friday, where are you? No marks.

CO-6

BUD MAN. ½-liter stoneware; 7¼″ (18.4 cm). Made as a promotional item for the Anheuser-Busch Brewing Co. Marked Ceramarte, Made in Brazil (28).

Dresden Art

CO-7
MONK. ½-liter porcelain; 9″ (22.9 cm). Contemporary full figure. Marked DRESDEN ART, MADE IN GERMANY (36).

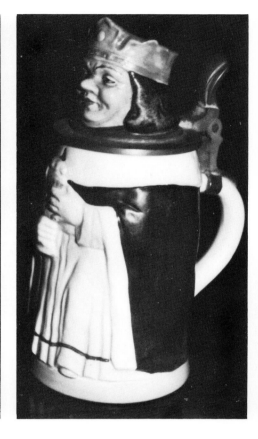

CO-8
GAMBRINUS. ½-liter porcelain; 8½″ (21.6 cm). This full figure of the little "King" clutchs a foaming brew with both hands. Marked DRESDEN ART, MADE IN GERMANY (36).

The "Indian" (*ECS*-182) and the "Bartender Pig" (*ECS*-52) appear to be made by the same maker.

Eckhardt & Engler

CO-9
MAN. ½-liter stoneware; 8½″ (21.6 cm). Marked Eckhardt & Engler (6), moldmark # 427, MADE IN WESTERN GERMANY. This stein was originally produced prior to World War I. It is shown in the 1914 catalog of Rosskopf & Gerz (38) with the same mold number. See "Old Catalogs."

CO-10

WOMAN. ½-liter stoneware; 7¾" (19.7 cm). This stern frau wears a hat that forms the lid. Her collar has the incised inscription: *"Behüt der Himmel dich das Guter vor einer solchen Schweigermutter."* (May the goodness of heaven protect you from such a mother-in-law.) MADE IN GERMANY, mold-mark # 429. Possible mate to the prior piece. It is also shown in the 1914 Rosskopf & Gerz (38) catalog with the same mold number. See "Old Catalogs."

CO-11
MAN AND WOMAN.

CO-12

MONK. ½-liter stoneware; 8¼" (21 cm). This smiling monk has a shaven head. His hands are tucked into the brown habit, almost as though it was a muff. The yellow striped cord tie around his waist has a dangling rosary. A black shoe sticks out. Manufactured ca. 1972. Marked Eckhardt & Engler (6), WESTERN GERMANY 0.5 L.

CO-13
MUNICH CHILD. ½-liter stoneware; 9″ (22.9 cm). This multicolored, somewhat crude figure holds three steins in the right hand. A bunch of radishes is held in the scapular, somewhat apron fashion. The pewter thumblift attaches through the pottery head. Very fine relief work, good detail. Date of manufacture, 1960s. Marked Eckhardt & Engler (6), moldmark # 551, WESTERN GERMANY 0.5 L. (all incised).

This stein is shown in the 1914 catalog of Rosskopf & Gerz (38) using the same mold number. See "Old Catalogs."

CO-14
HUNTER. ½-liter stoneware; 8½″ (21.6 cm). Pipe in right hand, rifle draped over left shoulder. Green "Robin Hood"-type hat. Colors are beige, brown, greys, and greens. Marked Eckhardt & Engler (6), moldmarked # 422, WESTERN GERMANY incised in the bottom. Also made by Werner Corzelius (29).

CO-15
DWARF. ½-liter stoneware; 9¼″ (23.5 cm). Sitting on a brown tree stump, smoking his long Bavarian pipe. Colors vary from his red cap, brown hair, and beard to his yellow jacket, grey stein and beige shoes. Marked Eckhardt & Engler (6), moldmark # 430 WESTERN GERMANY. A later version was made by Simon Peter Gerz (8).

CO-16, 17

MONKEY. ½-liter stoneware; 8½″ (21.6 cm). This brown sitting monkey holds a grey stein in his right hand, three radishes in his left. Marked Eckhardt & Engler (6), Moldmark # 421, WESTERN GERMANY, 0.5 L.

This stein is shown in the 1914 catalog of Rosskopf & Gerz (38) using the same mold number. See "Old Catalogs."

CO-18

<table>
<tr><td>**STUDENT,**
1131</td><td>**JÄGER,**
1130</td><td>**BRAUER,**
1132</td></tr>
</table>

CO-19
STUDENT.

CO-20
BRAUER (BREWER).

CO-21
NUREMBERG TOWER. ½-liter stoneware; 8½″ (21.6 cm). A highly-glazed brown variation of *ECS-416*, but with a matching stoneware lid. Marked Simon Peter Gerz (8b) W. Germany.

CO-22
FOOTBALL. ½-liter stoneware; 7¼″ (18.4 cm). A highly-glazed brown piece. Marked Simon Peter Gerz (8b), W. Germany.

CO-23
LION. ½-liter stoneware; 8″ (20.3 cm). This glossy brown animal holds the blue/white Bavarian shield. No marks. Simon Peter Gerz (8b)

CO-24
BARTENDER PIG. ½-liter stoneware; 8¼″ (21 cm). Similar to the piece described in *ECS*-52. No marks, but identified as Simon Peter Gerz (8b).

O-25

SOCCER BALL,   COQUETTE,   MAN,   MONK,   OWL,   SKULL.

CO-26

COQUETTE. ½-liter stoneware; 8″ (20.3 cm). Similar to *ECS*-291. This lovely young lady has a similar upswept braided hair lid, but the ribbon and earrings shown on the former version are missing on this glazed piece. No marks, only moldmark # 834. Matthias Girmscheid (25).

CO-27

OWL. ½-liter stoneware; 8″ (20.3 cm). Similar to *ECS*-122. This recent vintage stein from the Hoehr-Grenzhausen area possibly was made by more than one manufacturer as it has been identified in both the catalogs of Thewalt (7) and Girmscheid (25). No marks, only moldmark # 740, GERMANY incised in the bottom. Some pieces read "Made in Germany Western" incised into the base. It has been seen in many shades of browns and greens.

CO-28

DUCK,   **MONKEY,**   **FROG,**   **FROG,**   **MONKEY,**   **FOX.**

DUCK. ½-liter stoneware; 10″ (25.4 cm). Highly glazed. No marks, only moldmark #839. Matthias Girmscheid (25).

CO-30

FROG. ½-liter stoneware; 7¼″ (18.4 cm). Similar to *ECS*-439. In varying gradations of greens and yellows. The belly inscription reads: *Der Frosch quack wenn er sich labt."* (The frog croaks when he refreshes himself.) No marks, only moldmark # 825, GERMANY. Manufactured by Matthias Girmscheid (25).

CO-31

GENTLEMAN FOX. ½-liter stoneware; 10½″ (26.7 cm). Sitting on his haunches, this "hunter" has a beige walking stick tucked under his right arm, a similarly colored sack in his right. Three brown birds peck away at the sack. Written along the base is the saying *"WAIDMANN LIEBER WAIDMANN SCHAU, DER FUCHS ALS JÄGER IST AUCH SCHLAU."* (Hunter, dear hunter, look, the fox is as a hunter.) This is a copy of an earlier stein made by the same maker. No marks, only moldmark # 827. Matthias Girmscheid (25).

CO-32
MONKEY. ½-liter stoneware; 8¼″ (21 cm). This casual "hobo" sports a tattered brown jacket, with green lapels. On his back are two inscriptions: "*Wird der Affen bierfass gross,*" (When the drunkeness becomes as large as a barrel) and "*Ist auch gleich der teufel los*" (Soon the devil will also be loose). No marks, only moldmark # 828. Matthias Girmscheid (25).

CO-33   DOG,   ROOSTER,   DOG,   RAM,   MONKEY,   FROG.

CO-34

ROOSTER. ½-liter stoneware; 8¾″ (22.2 cm). Colored various shades of reddish brown, he holds a grey clock by both claws. The comb and wattle are a bright red. No marks, only moldmark # 832. Identified as Matthias Girmscheid (25).

RAM. ½-liter stoneware; 8″ (20.3 cm). Similar to *ECS*-67. No marks, only moldmark # 831. Matthias Girmscheid (25).

CO-35

MONKEY. ½-liter stoneware; 8½″ (21.6 cm). This brown little fellow has an inebriated smile typical of the many monkeys pictured in *ECS*-33–47. He holds a grey beaker and pitcher in his hands. No marks, only moldmark # 833. Matthias Girmscheid (25).

CO-36

SOCCER BALL. ½-liter stoneware; 4¾″ (12.1 cm). Modern version (right) made by Matthias Girmscheid mold # 315, alongside *ECS*-115 made by Steinzeugwerke (23).

219

CO-37
BAVARIAN HUNTER. ½-liter stoneware; 8″ (20.3 cm). Pipe in one hand, a rifle slung over his left shoulder. No marks. Matthias Girmscheid (25).

Rastal-Werk

CO-38
Some examples of recent porcelain steins being reproduced for RASTAL-WERK (24).

From left: BISMARCK (See *ECS*-132), 7″ (17.8 cm); HEIDELBERG STUDENT (*ECS*-190), 8½″ (21.6 cm); GENTLEMAN RABBIT (*ECS*-63), 8″ (20.3 cm); DRUNKEN MONKEY (*ECS*-39), 7¼″ (18.4 cm); and HOPS LADY (*ECS*-288).

CO-39
MUNICH CHILD. ½- and ¼-liter porcelain. Made of bisque with multicolored hand painting. Lithophane in bottom shows "Bavaria with Lion." Pewter thumb-rest depicts the twin domes of Munich's Frauenkirche.

CO-40

FRAUENKIRCHE TOWERS. ½-liter and 1-liter porcelain. A modern stylized version of the towers pictured in *ECS*-419, 420. Multicolored hand painted, topped by a beautifully detailed pewter "onion" dome. Rosette hinge and large, oval thumbrest depicting the Munich Child. Marked Rastal 1976 (24). Also "Turm Frauenkirche München Porzellan" in green lettering; "Handgemalt D. Wagner" (the decorator) in black script. From left above—brick red coloring; white; grey stoneware with blue and manganese painting. Salt-glazed.

CO-41

MUNICH CHILD. ½-liter porcelain; 9½" (24.1 cm). Well-made copy, 1976, for Rastal of Hoehr-Grenzhausen. Twin towers (Church of Our Lady) thumblift. Black robe and hood with yellow scapular and red lining. Lifelike face and hands. Naturally colored pretzel and radish. Also manufactured in ¼-liter size. Cuff linings can be either red or blue. Lithophane of the Bavaria Statue with Ruhmeshalle in the background. Signed "Handgemalt D. Wagner."

CO-42
MUNICH CHILD. ½-liter porcelain. The meeting of the "new" and "old." The contemporary Child on the left holds a pretzel in the right hand, radishes in the left. Whereas the older, more pensive figure on the right has only the radishes in the left hand. For description of the 1976 version, please see the prior stein.

CO-43
MUNICH CHILD. ½-liter porcelain; 9½″ (24.1 cm). Similar to the prior stein, except all white. Manufactured in 1976 for Rastal (24).

CO-44
A Recent Rastal Ad.

Hummelwerk (Goebel)

CO-45
MONK. ½-liter porcelain; 6½″ (16.5 cm). This flesh-toned bulbous bisque figural (brown robe) was manufactured around 1950 by Goebel (26a).

CO-46
MONK. ¼-liter porcelain; 4¼″ 11.4 cm). A smaller bisque companion to the prior stein. Manufactured ca. 1960s by Goebel (26b). The moldmark # T 74/0 is also incised in the base.

CO-47
MONKS. ¼-liter porcelain; ½-liter porcelain.

CO-48

Goebel Merkelbach

CO-48
GNOMES. ½-liter. Left, Red Hat # 250556; middle, Blue Hat # 250557; right, Green Hat # 250558.

CO-49
GNOMES. ½-liter # 250559 playing accordian, # 250560 taking a bath, # 250561 shoemaker.

CO-49

CO-50

CO-50
BEARDED PIXIE. ½-liter earthenware; 9″ (22.9 cm). No marks. Distributed by Hachiya Brothers Company (33), #51685 in their catalog.

CO-51

CO-51
ELEPHANT. ½-liter earthenware; 8″ (20.3 cm). No marks. Distributed by Hachiya Brothers Company (33), # 51687 in their catalog.

51688 51685 51692 51683 51691

51678 51684 51686 51682 51680

51690 51681 51679 51687 51689

51693 51694 51695 51677

51685-M 51692-M 51691-M 51690-M 51689-M

Hachiya Brothers Company

CO-52
Recent Ad.

CO-53
OWL. ½-liter earthenware; 8½″ (21.6 cm). No marks. Hachiya Brothers Company (33), # 51679.

CO-54
BARTENDER PIG. ½-liter earthenware; 9″ (22.9 cm). Similar to the pig manufactured by Gerz and to *ECS*-52. Hachiya Brothers Company (33), # 51681.

CO-55
SOLDIER. ½-liter earthenware; 9″ (22.9 cm). Dress cap and beard. Music box base. No marks. Hachiya Brothers Company. (33), # 51694.

CO-56
SOLDIER. ½-liter earthenware; 9″ (22.9 cm). Peaked cap. Music box base. No marks. Hachiya Brothers Company (33), # 51695.

CO-57
LAUREL AND HARDY. ½-liter earthenware; 9″ (22.9 cm). No marks. Hachiya Brothers Company (33).

CO-58
ROYAL MOUNTED POLICE. ½-liter earthenware; 9″ (22.9 cm). No marks. Hachiya Brothers Company (33).

CO-59
COLONIST. ¾-liter earthenware; 10″ (25.4 cm). This full figure is holding a mug of beer in his right hand, a cane in his left. Green coat, blue knickers, yellow and white trim and ruffles. Thumblift is attached to handle and lid by screws. Hachiya Brothers Company (33).

CO-60
ROOSTER, DUCK, and EAGLE. ½-liter earthenware; 8″ (20.3 cm). Hinge attaches to top of handle with a simple bolt. Hachiya Brothers Company (33b).

CO-61
SEÑOR WITH GUITAR. ½-liter earthenware; 9″ (22.9 cm). No marks. Distributed by Hachiya Brothers Company (33), # 51677 in their catalog.

CO-62
DOG ON PEDESTAL. ½-liter earthenware; 11¼″ (28.6 cm). No marks. Base contains a music box. Catalog # 51689-M. Also comes with no pedestal, catalog # 51689. Distributed by Hachiya Brothers Company (33).

CO-63
THREE HEADS. ½-liter earthenware; 6½″ (16.5 cm). From left: Man with Bowtie, Policeman, Smiling Man. No pewter attachments. Marked Stangl Pottery (34).

CO-64
SIX REINHOLD MERKELBACH STEINS.

Reinhold Merkelbach

CO-65

BARMAN. ½-liter stoneware; 8″ (20.3 cm). Holding a grey beaker in his right hand, a pitcher in his left. A red scarf wraps around his blue/grey shirt. A large brown apron encircles his broad girth. Viewed from the side he appears to be walking. No marks. Reinhold Merkelbach (5d).

CO-66

HOBO. ½-liter stoneware; 8½″ (21.6 cm). Holding a hot dog in his right hand, an umbrella in his left. This grizzly-faced character still sports a red boutonniere and a reddish-brown bedroll across his back. No marks. But identified as Reinhold Merkelbach (5d).

CO-67

ACCORDION MAN. ½-liter stoneware; 9″ (22.9 cm). Sporting a forest green hat, this sitting man is happily playing his accordion. Stout flesh-colored legs stick out of his grey Lederhosen. No marks, old moldmark #4156. Identified as Reinhold Merkelbach (5d).

CO-68

FUNNELMAN. ½-liter stoneware; 8″ (20.3 cm). The body of this stein is formed by the brown staves of a barrel. In his left hand he carries a black lit lantern, a foaming tankard of beer is in his other hand. The grey funnel lid is supported by a pewter rim. Marked Reinhold Merkelbach (5d), moldmark #4127, made in Germany.

CO-69

MONK. ½-liter stoneware, 7″ (17.8 cm). This rotund man of the cloth (or hops?) is wearing a brownish red robe with a white rope sash. Face and hands are skin-toned, with ruddy cheeks. A black Bible in his right hand, grey foamy stein in the other. Marked Reinhold Merkelbach (5d), moldmark #4107, made in Germany. This stein was also made with a music box in the lid that plays "How Dry I Am" when opened.

CO-70

TYROLIAN HUNTER. ½-liter stoneware; 8¼″ (21 cm). This seated man is holding a rifle in one hand, a glass in the other. His hat and coat are green, with a brown collar. He wears a red vest with a yellow collar and buttons. Marked Reinhold Merkelbach (5d), made in Germany.

CO-71

GENTLEMAN RABBIT. ½-liter porcelain; 8½″ (21.6 cm). A fine modern-day reproduction of *ECS-64*. As seen in the original advertising, this piece was referred to as "Hunter." Many collectors have inadvertently paid top dollar for this piece and the other three, marked R.P.M. (11) This brightly colored version is not as well done as *ECS-64*.

CO-72

BISMARCK. ½-liter porcelain; 7″ (17.8 cm). Another reproduction of a fine old character stein (*ECS-133*). Close examination reveals harsher coloring than the original soft beige/browns. The porcelain is very heavy. Marked with a dark blue crosshatch.

CO-73

DRUNKEN MONKEY. ½-liter porcelain; 7½″ (19.1 cm). This reproduction of the late 1940s looks quite similar to *ECS-39*. Again, harsher coloring is noted on this well-made piece. Marked R.P.M. (11).

Albert Jacob Thewalt

CO-74

CO-75
#9001
Wurst-
meier

#9002
Münchener
Kindl

#9003
Zenzi

#9004
Meier-
Gustel

#9005
Hessen-
Grit

#9006
Hein-Mück

CO-76
ZENSI. ½-liter stoneware; 7¼″ (18.4 cm). Marked Thewalt (7d), Western Germany, original model.

CO-77
SAILOR. ½-liter stoneware; 7¼″ (18.4 cm). A fine reproduction of *ECS*-332. Also made in overall blue coloring. Marked Thewalt (7d), Western Germany.

Miscellaneous

CO-78
OWL. ½-liter stoneware; 8½″ (21.6 cm). No marks, only "Hand made in Germany." Distributed by Tripar International.

Both the Owl and Lion were made by Gerlich in Hillsceid u. Koblenz, West Germany. The factory is no longer in operation.

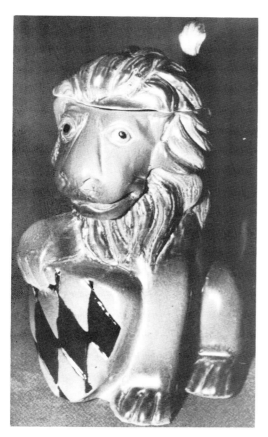

LION. ½-liter stoneware; 8¼″ (21 cm). No marks, only "Hand made in Germany." Distributed by Tripar International.

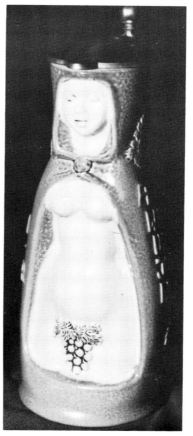

CO-80

WINE WITCH. ¾-liter stoneware; 9¼″ (23.5 cm). A very interesting "controversial" pitcher. Inscribed along the sides is *"Alter wein und junger weiber"* (Old wine and young women) and *"Sind die Besten zeit—vertreiber"* (Are the best ways to spend your time). Original King #3, and the mold-mark #288.

This piece was made by Wuerfel & Mueller (King Works) in Hoehr-Grenzhausen.

CO-81

TYROLEAN MAN. ½-liter earthenware. 8″ (20.3 cm). Originally made without pewter; attachments added. Coloring in greens and whites. No marks.

CO-82
TURK. ½-liter earthenware. This contemporary green and white figural does not have any pewter attachments. No marks.

CO-83
SCOTSMAN. ½-liter earthenware. Similar coloring and workmanship to the prior. No marks. No pewter attachments.

CO-84
CHINESE MAN. ½-liter earthenware; 7½″ (19.1 cm). Originally made without pewter. Attachment added later from right arm to shoulder. No marks.

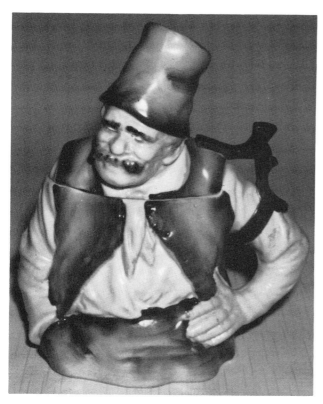

CO-85
TURKISH PEASANT. ½-liter earthenware; 8¼″ (21 cm). Copy of *ECS*-161. Originally without pewter; attachment added at a later date. No marks.

CO-86
TURKISH PEASANTS. Musterschutz, *ECS*-161 on left, copy on right.

CO-87
ALPINE MOUNTAINEER. ½-liter earthenware; 8″ (20.3 cm). Another copy of *ECS*-165. Originally without pewter. Attachment added later. No marks.

237

CO-88
ALPINE MOUNTAINEERS. ½-liter. Musterschutz, *ECS*-165 on left, copy on right.

CO-89
ALPINE MOUNTAINEERS. ½-liter earthenware. Similar copies. Pewter attachments on the left. No marks, only GERMANY stamped on the bottom.

CO-90
DEVIL. ½-liter stoneware; 7½″ (19.1 cm). An unusual satanic stein. He holds a pitchfork in his right hand. His "tail" forms the handle. A gold *D* attaches to his pants with a gold safety pin. A right hoof and left foot stick out of his pants. No marks, only MADE IN WESTERN GERMANY.

CO-91
SKULL ON BOOK. ½-liter stoneware; 5¼″ (13.3 cm). A recent version of *ECS*-400. Cruder than the original bisque porcelain piece. No marks, only made in Germany, ASN.

CO-92
SKULLS ON BOOKS. Left, the contemporary skull, *ECS*-400 on right.

CO-93
MUNICH CHILD. ½-liter stoneware; 10¼″ (26 cm). This "kindl" is heavily glazed inside and out—presumably to make it look like porcelain. Music box base. No marks. Age questionable, possibly made prior to W.W. II.

CO-94

DRINKING HORN. ½-liter glass; 6½" (16.5 cm). Commercial drinking vessel manufactured for the Anheuser Busch Co. Decal of "Budweiser Champion Clydesdales." Horn handle. No marks. Also sold in gift shops minus any decal decorations.

CO-95

METTLACH ABBEY. 2-liter stoneware; 12" (30.5 cm). This limited edition was made by Villeroy & Boch (16b) for the annual convention of Stein Collectors International. The off-white stein (5 gold-leaf bands) is incised with the inscription "12th Annual Convention S.C.I. Mettlach 13th–16th July 1978."

CO-96

STATUE OF LIBERTY. ½-liter stoneware; 7¼" (18.4 cm) to top of highest spike. Another very limited edition commemorative stein (300 pieces) made for the 8th annual convention of Stein Collectors International, held in New York City 18–21 July 1974. Marked Ceramarte (28), Made in Brazil. Original steins are given to all attendees of the S.C.I. annual conventions. This was the first character stein issued as a convention stein.

CO-97

MANNEKEN-PIS. ½-liter earthenware; 10½″ (26.7 cm). This iridescent-beige full figure depicts the famous nude caught in the pose of relieving himself. There is a small 17th-century bronze statue which forms the focal point of a small fountain in the Belgian city of Brussels (CO-98). The bronze was made by the Flemish sculptor, Jerome Duquesnoy. No marks, only MADE IN GERMANY WESTERN [*sic*].

CO-98

MANNEKIN-PIS. 17th-century bronze statue, Brussels, Belgium.

CO-98

Stein Related

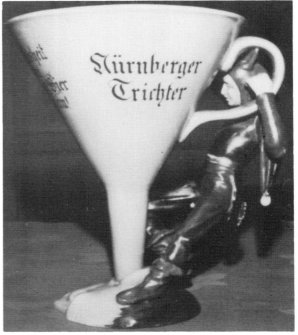

SR-1

NUREMBERG FUNNEL GOBLET. Porcelain; ³⁄₁₀-liter. 6¾″. A fine compliment to the Nuremberg Trichter (*ECS-445*). The handle is formed by a finely detailed red and black jester. The base is in the shape of the side of a man's head, with the funnel sticking in his ear. This signifies the funnel of knowledge being poured into his brain. The verse on the front reads: "*Finst gols man Weisheit durch mich ein, Fitzt diene ich dem Wier u. auch dem Wein!*" (Once upon a time they poured wisdom through me, now I serve beer and wine!). Marked F&M/N 5021 (22), GES. GESCH, and the cross-hatch (1a). PREISCEKRÖNT (fixed price).*

SR-2

SITTING ALLIGATOR SALT SHAKER. Porcelain; 3¼″ (8.3 cm). A finely detailed mate to *ECS-430*. The salt shaker (right), seen here with a small (3½″) crudely constructed miniature alligator stein has a cork-stopper in the base. No marks, only the # 45.

*Made by Schierholz and Sohn.

SR-3
FOOTBALL TOBACCO JAR. Porcelain; 7¾″ (19.7 cm). A rare companion piece to the football series shown in *ECS*-96. The football player wears the jersey of the University of Pennsylvania (the school crest appears on the reverse side). The decal is signed "F. Earl Christy." The lid finial is in the shape of a cigar butt. Colored beige/brown with a silver lustre pedestal base. Marked T. MADDOCKS SONS CO. (27).

SR-4
WRAP AROUND ALLIGATOR TOBACCO JAR. Bisque porcelain. A beautiful mate to the ³⁄₁₀-liter stein (*ECS*-428). No marks.

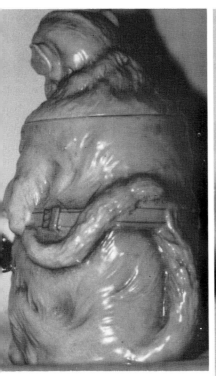

SR-5, 6
DRUNKEN MONKEY TOBACCO JAR. Porcelain; 7½″ (19.1 cm). A fine mate to *ECS*-39. The tail curls under the belt. No pewter rim is seen on this version. Marked Musterschutz (10a).*

Made by Schierholz and Sohn.

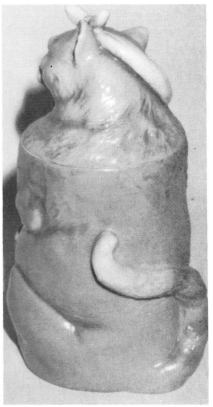

SR-7

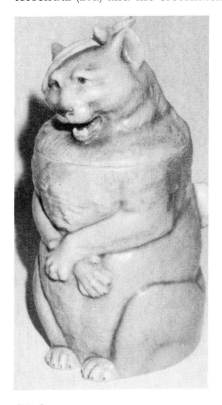

SR-8

SR-7, 8
CAT WITH HANGOVER TOBACCO JAR.
Porcelain; 8″ (20.3 cm). A delicate honey-beige brown jar to compliment *ECS*-5. Once again the pewter rim is lacking. The lid is not slammed down (as on a stein), so it was not necessary to place any pewterwork on the tobacco jars. Marked Musterschutz (10a) and the crosshatch (1a).*

SR-9
SINGING PIG TOBACCO JAR. Porcelain; 6½″ (16.5 cm). Comparable to the prior jar, this version, lacking any pewter rim, is similar to *ECS*-55. Marked Musterschutz (10a) and the crosshatch (1a).*

*Made by Schierholz and Sohn.

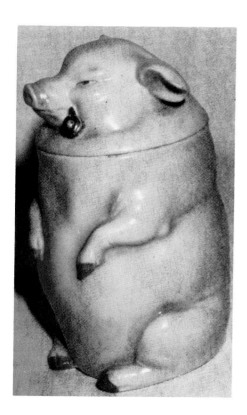

SR-10
PIG WITH PIPE TOBACCO JAR. Porcelain; 6½″
(16.5 cm). Similar to *ECS*-49. In the beige/browns
of Musterschutz (10a).*

SR-11

SR-13
TURKISH PEASANT TOBACCO JAR. Porcelain;
9″ (22.9 cm). Similar beige/cream coloring as *ECS*-
161. No pewter attachments. Marked Musterschutz (10a) and the crosshatch (1a).*

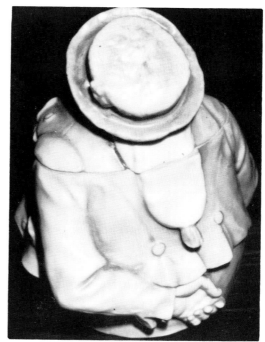

SR-12

SR-11, 12
BUERGERMEISTER TOBACCO JAR. Porce-
lain, 7″ (17.8 cm). Similar to *ECS*-163. Marked
Musterschutz (10a).*

*Made by Schierholz and Sohn.

SR-14
ALPINE MOUNTAINEER TOBACCO JAR.
Porcelain; 7½″ (19.1 cm). Similar to *ECS-165*.
Marked Musterschutz (10a) and the crosshatch
(1a).*

SR-15
ENLISTED MAN TOBACCO JAR. Porcelain;
4½″ (11.4 cm). A comical slightly tipsy young man.
Seen here with a similar stein (see "Military").
No marks, only the inked # 62, GESCHÜTZT.
Also seen in a two-toned blue coloring. Marked
1670 34 & 13.

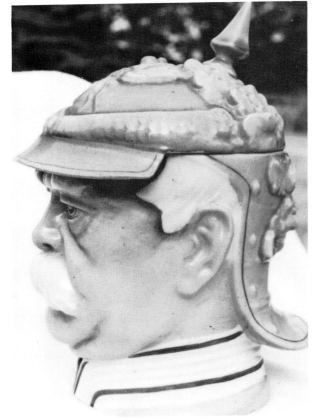

SR-16
BISMARCK TOBACCO JAR. Porcelain; 7¼″ (18.4
cm). Similar to *ECS-134*. Marked Musterschutz
(10a), and the crosshatch (1a).*

*Made by Schierholz and Sohn. **246**

BISMARCK TOBACCO JAR. Earthenware; 8¼″ (21 cm). An enameled variation of *ECS*-134. No marks, only the moldmark # 3943 83.

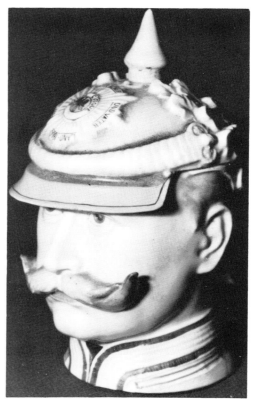

SR-18
WILHELM II TOBACCO JAR. Porcelain; 6½″ (16.5 cm). The Kaiser is depicted here with his Garde du Corp helmet, but lacking the large eagle commonly seen on the *ECS*-150 version. Marked Musterschutz (10a) and the crosshatch (1a).*

SR-19
SKULL CUP AND SAUCER. Bisque porcelain. A fine way to sip tea(!) in the morning. Marked Ernst Bohne (2).

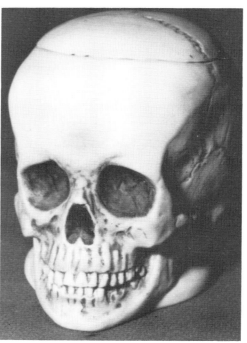

SR-20
SKULL TOBACCO JAR. Bisque porcelain; 4½″ (11.4 cm). Fabricated ca. 1906. No marks.

*Made by Schierholz and Sohn.

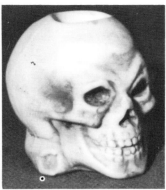

SR-21
SKULL MATCH HOLDER. Bisque porcelain; 2″ (5.1 cm). Mate to the prior tobacco jar. No marks.

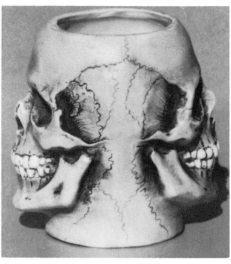

SR-22
BACK-TO-BACK SKULLS TOBACCO JAR. Bisque porcelain; 4½″ (11.4 cm). Similar to *ECS-407* and 408. The texture of the porcelain is very much like the feel of real boney tissue. Finely detailed beige suture lines. No marks, but similar in appearance to the quality of Ernst Bohne (2).

SR-23
SKULL STEIN, MATCHHOLDER, AND TOBACCO JAR. *ECS-402* with matching accessories.

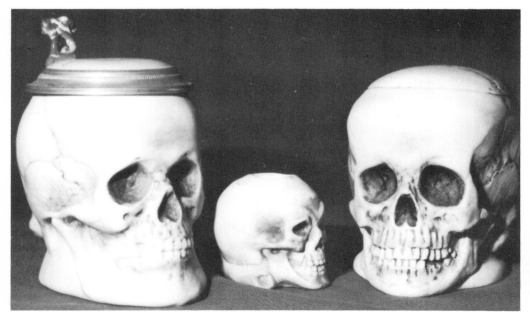

SR-24
CAROLINE TOBACCO JAR. Porcelain; 6″ (15.2 cm). A definite likeness to the beautiful *ECS-292*. Marked with the Musterschutz (10a) and crosshatch (1a).*

*Made by Schierholz and Sohn.

HOPS LADY TOBACCO JAR. Stoneware; 6″ (15.2 cm). A fine match to *ECS-289*. No marks, only the moldmark # 1424, GERMANY. Identified as Steinzeugwerke (23).

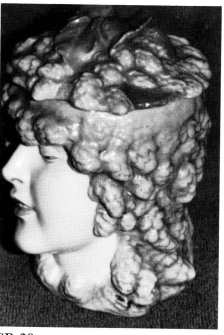

SR-26
HOPS LADY TOBACCO JAR. Porcelain; 6″ (15.2 cm). Similar to *ECS-288*. Marked with the cross-hatch (1a) and Musterschutz (10a).*

SR-27
SAD RADISH SCHNAPPES SET. Porcelain. A green-leafed stopper inserts into the bulbous base. Root-like feet support the bottle. The two matching beakers complement the set. Please refer to *ECS-255*. No marks.*

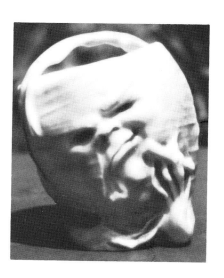

SR-28
SAD RADISH BASKET. Porcelain; 3¼″ (8.3 cm). The same texture and workmanship is found in this tiny basket. The beige/brown piece has vines that form a "hand" holding a cigar. Marked Musterschutz (10b).*

*Made by Schierholz and Sohn.

SR-29
SAD RADISH MUSTARD JAR. Porcelain; 3½″ (8.9 cm). Similar to *ECS-255*. This piece was made as a Happy Radish also. Marked Musterschutz (10a).*

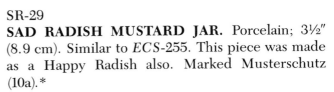

SR-30
SAD RADISH SALT AND PEPPER SHAKERS. Porcelain; 3¾″ (9.5 cm). The holes are different sizes, the *P* marked in black ink. No marks.*

SR-31, 32, 33
DUTCH BOY BANK. Porcelain; 8½″ (21.6 cm). Similar contemporary replica of the Dutch Boy (*ECS-166*), except coloration is a light blue and white (see "Figurals"). When lid is opened, the internal is enclosed except for the coin slot. The bottom has a large opening (fitted with rubber stopper) for removing the coins. The pewter attachment appears to be fastened to the lid by an epoxy. No marks.

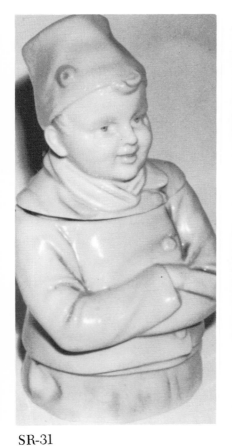

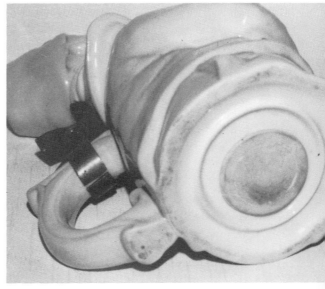

SR-31

SR-32

SR-33

*Made by Schierholz an

SR-34
MUSTERSCHUTZ DUTCH BOY and DUTCH GIRL (*ECS*-166) flank newer bank.

SR-35
IRON MAIDEN FROM NUREMBERG FIGURAL. Pewter; 5½″ (14 cm). The ghastly story of the torture chamber depicted by this stein is detailed in *ECS*-239. A matching "Maiden" is shown alongside the stein in this photo. The hinged front doors open to reveal the sharp spikes, as in the actual chamber. The true "Maiden" measures approximately eight feet in height.

SR-36
SATAN CIGAR AND MATCHHOLDER. Porcelain; 8″ (20.3 cm). Similar in coloring and texture to the bisque drinking vessels shown in *ECS*-412. The head-opening allows an area to hold cigars. Long curved fingernails. Marked Ernst Bohne (2a).

SR-37
SATAN MATCHHOLDERS. Bisque porcelain. Very lifelike accessories to compliment the Satan steins (*ECS*-411). The larger holder (left) measures 3½″ (8.9 cm) to the tip of his horns. The smaller young devil, sticking his tongue out at the world, measures 2″ (5.1 cm). Both have white match "strikeplates" along the rear surface. No marks, but similar to Ernst Bohne (2).

SR-38
BARREL MUSTARD JAR. Stoneware; 3¾″ (9.5 cm). A stein-shaped barrel, light blue with dark blue bands and handle. Pewter attachments. Marked Villeroy & Boch (16a).

SR-39
INDIAN HEAD MATCHHOLDER. Bisque porcelain; 3″. Indian head with striker in rear. No marks. Probably Ernst Bohne (2).

SR-40
MUNICH CHILD MATCHHOLDER. Earthenware; 4″ (10.2 cm). "*Scho leer?*" (Empty already?) written on the side of the box # 547 impressed on the rear. No marks.

SR-41
MUNICH CHILD MATCHHOLDER. Bisque porcelain; 5″ (12.7 cm). No marks.

SR-42
INDIAN CHIEF CIGAR HOLDER. Bisque porcelain; 5″ (12.7 cm). Marked Ernst Bohne (2).

SR-42

SR-43
INDIAN CHIEF TOBACCO JAR. Bisque porcelain; 5¾″ (14.6 cm). Very similar to the prior cigar holder. No marks.

SR-43

SR-44
INDIAN CHIEF MATCHHOLDER. Bisque porcelain. Shown here (left) with the matching pipe and tobacco jar. Marked Ernst Bohne (2).

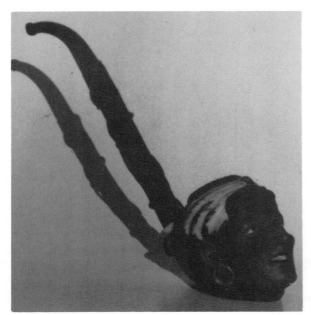

SR-45
INDIAN CHIEF PIPE. Bisque porcelain. The bowl of this pipe has the fine lifelike detail as found on the corresponding steins (*ECS-274*).

SR-46
MUNICH CHILD PIPE. Porcelain. This ornately colored Child resembles many of the steins depicted in that chapter. The head of the Child is hinged to permit an opening. A silver rim around the lid attaches to a silver "thumblift." The Muenchener Kindl alone measures approximately 3½″ (8.9 cm); the entire bowl, 4¼″ (11.3 cm). The pipe is 18″ (46 cm) in length.

SR-47
SEATED BILLY GOAT PIPE. Porcelain. Similar to *ECS-65*. A steel hinge attaches the lid to the stem of this unusual pipe bowl.*

SR-48
BISMARCK PIPE. Porcelain. A fine pipe to smoke while sipping a sudsy brew out of your *ESC-132*. The hinged helmet permits placement of tobacco.

Probably made by the same maker as those marked Musterschutz (10).*

*Made by Schierholz and Sohn.

49

SR-49, 50

MUETZE ASHTRAY. Porcelain; 4″ (10.2 cm) in diameter. An unusual variation of the enlisted man's military cap (see *ECS*-324, 325 and the "Military" section). The decal reads: "*Kriegserinnerung. Gott mitt uns 1914.*" (A souvenir of the war. God (is) with us. 1914). No marks.

SR-50

SR-51

RENAISSANCE LADY BEAKER. ½-liter stoneware; 8″ (20.3 cm). Wearing the costume of a 16th century wealthy young hostess, this drinking vessel has to be inverted to drink out of her hoopskirt. A detailed explanation of this *Stehseidein* can be found in *Prosit* (# 70, December 1982, page 978) by Dr. James Gruhl. No marks. Identified as Villeroy & Boch (16), moldmark # 5045.

255

OLD CATALOGS

THIS SECTION, SHOWING COPIES OF ACTUAL STEIN FACTORY CATALOGS, IS BY FAR THE MOST important chapter of this book. Here we can actually see and identify many of the steins shown in the various categories.

In examining these catalog pages, we must bear in mind a few important facts relating to these factories and their practices. When we look at a section of say, *Steinzeugwerke,* we must realize that we are looking at merely a portion of only one of their catalogs. They undoubtedly made many more steins and issued many more catalogs. It would be sensational if we could put together *all* of the catalogs showing *all* of the steins made by even one of these stein makers. Through these very partial excerpts, we can see trends and analyze styles and can sometimes take the liberty of attributing other steins to these factories.

We also often find some of these same stein bodies with different lid variations. This, we find, is quite common. We also find that, over the years, these steins are shown and made with minor body variations. In some instances, a beer stein will be added to the figure's hand, a pipe might be deleted, or a different hat might be found. Often, the same mold number may be present on this variation. A classic example of a change in a mold would be the "Beehive" (MI-1) which was made one time with twenty bees and, at another time with seventeen bees. What Merkelbach & Wick did was change the mold, either adding or subtracting three bees.

Errors sometimes do occur in these old catalogs and we cannot accept them as gospel. In the *J. W. Remy* catalog, the mold numbers of the "Military Monkey" and the "Dog" are reversed.

In the *Reinhold Hanke* catalog, the name of Bismarck was misspelled as "Bismark." I doubt that these factories bothered to be too careful with these steins, as they were not regarded too highly at that time by their makers. Very few were used for drinking purposes and many were poor sellers. Very often these makers didn't bother to even mark the steins with their trademarks. Also, many are found without even liter markings.

Lastly, just because we can identify a stein from a catalog page does not mean that they were the sole makers of that stein or that they even were one of the makers. As we can see, most of these stein factories were located within a small area of the Westerwald region of Germany. There was much interchanging of designs, selling of molds, intermarriage of the families, and change of personnel within this small area. This led to much confusion as to who actually made any particular stein at any given time, even though we can identify the stein from a definite factory catalog.

Here are but some of the possibilities that might have arisen which can confuse the issue:

1. While one factory may have made a certain stein, another might have acted as a selling agent and included it in their catalog and even added their name to the stein base.

2. After the stein was made by one factory, the mold may have been sold or traded to another and produced by them at a later date.
3. The design for the mold may have been the property of the artist who, when moving from one factory to another, may have taken his design with him and recreated it with his new employer.

One example we find of this is the "Dutch Girl" (FI-67) which is shown in the *Reinhold Merkelbach* catalog, yet is found with the Merkelbach & Wick (4a) mark. Also, steins originally shown and made by *Rosskopf & Gerz* were first given to *Eckhardt & Engler* to act as their distributor, and later sold the molds to them. These items were produced by Eckhardt & Engler for many years, and some of them were made until after World War II.

Many steins depicted in the various catagories are labeled "Identified as _____." This is arrived at by either finding them in an old catalog or by studying designs and styles used by these factories. In some cases, we may be wrong, but overall, I think we can safely make these remarks.

It is our hope and desire to unearth additional original catalog pages and, in doing so, add more knowledge and to be able to identify many more "unknown" steins.

Marzi & Remy

HÖHR

Nº 466

Nº 539

Nº 549

Nº 582

20 Cent. h.

25 Cent. h.
Bierseidel ½ Ltr mit Beschlag.

20 Ct.h.

24 Cent.h.
Kaiser Wilhelm I

Nº 582A

Nº 583

Nº 584

Nº 585

21½ Cent.h.
Kaiser Wilhelm II

24 Cent. h.
Kaiser Friedrich III

22½ Ct. h.
Bismark

22 Cent. h
Moltke

Nº 642

Nº 871

Nº 875

Nº 895

24 Cent. h.

20 Cent. h.

21 Cent h

23½ Cent.h.

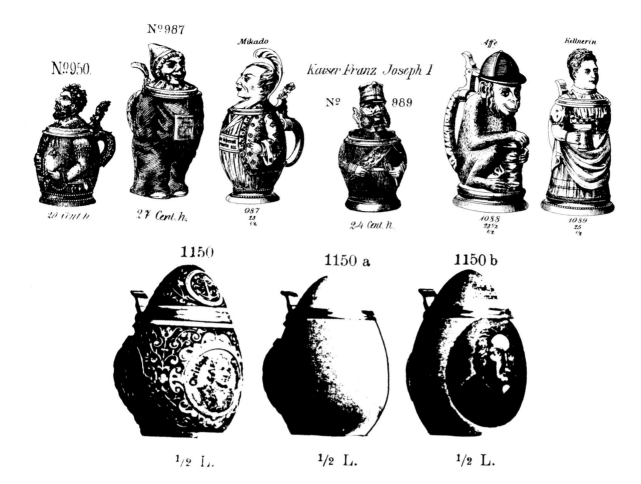

No950.

No987

Mikado

Kaiser Franz Joseph I

No 989

Affe

Kellnerin

20 Cent. h.

27 Cent. h.

987
23
1/2

24 Cent. h.

1088
23 1/2
1/2

1089
25
1/2

1150

1150 a

1150 b

1/2 L.

1/2 L.

1/2 L.

nhold Merkelbach

J. W. Remy

5 — ¹/₂ L.   766 — ¹/₂ L.   767 — ¹/₂ L.   768 — ¹/₂ L.   769 — ¹/₂ L.   770 — ¹/₂ L.

J. W. REMY

Manufacturers of Beersteins

(22b) Hoehr-Grenzhausen

P. O. B. 18

• GERMANY •

1195 — 1 Ltr.   976 — ³/₄ Ltr.   1249 — ¹/₂ Ltr.   1132 — ¹/₂ Ltr.   1176 — ¹/₂ Ltr.

1257 — 1 Ltr.   1300 — ³/₄ Ltr.   1298 — 1 Ltr.   1246 — 1 Ltr.   1259 — 1 Ltr.

1236 — ¹/₂ Ltr.   1282 — ¹/₂ Ltr.   1280 — ¹/₂ Ltr.   1281 — ¹/₂ Ltr.   1332 — ¹/₂ Ltr.

Figurenseidel, ½ L. Flach- und Hohlboden Modern.

420	421	422	423	424
425	427	428	429	430
431	426	550	551	609
439	446	448	457	586	588

Flachboden

Hohlboden

Liste **J. B.**

Steinzeugwerke Höhr-Grenzhausen
G. m. b. H.
in **Höhr bei Coblenz**

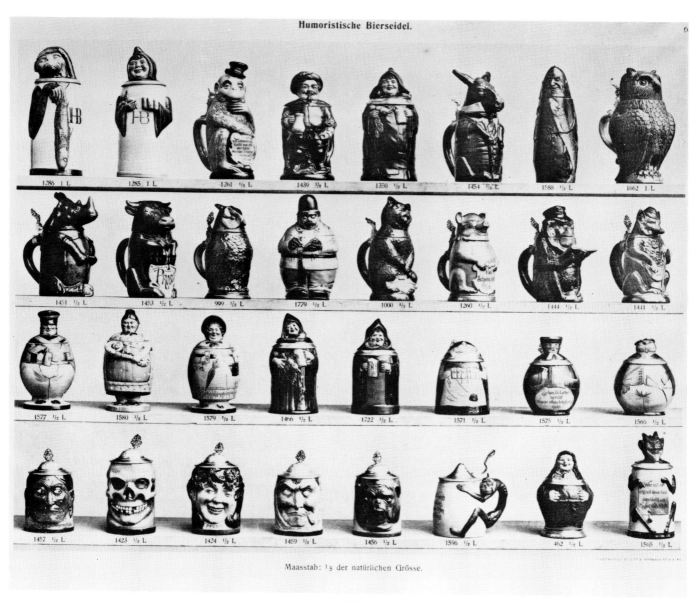

Humoristische Bierseidel.

Maasstab: ⅕ der natürlichen Grösse.

1402 ½ L

1771
Diogenes

1257
Affen

1769
Bergseidel

1251
Stemmseidel

1730 ½ L
Studenten-Mumie

1186 1½ L

1730 ½ L
Fussballspieler

1134
Kegel

1663 ½ L
Kegelseidel

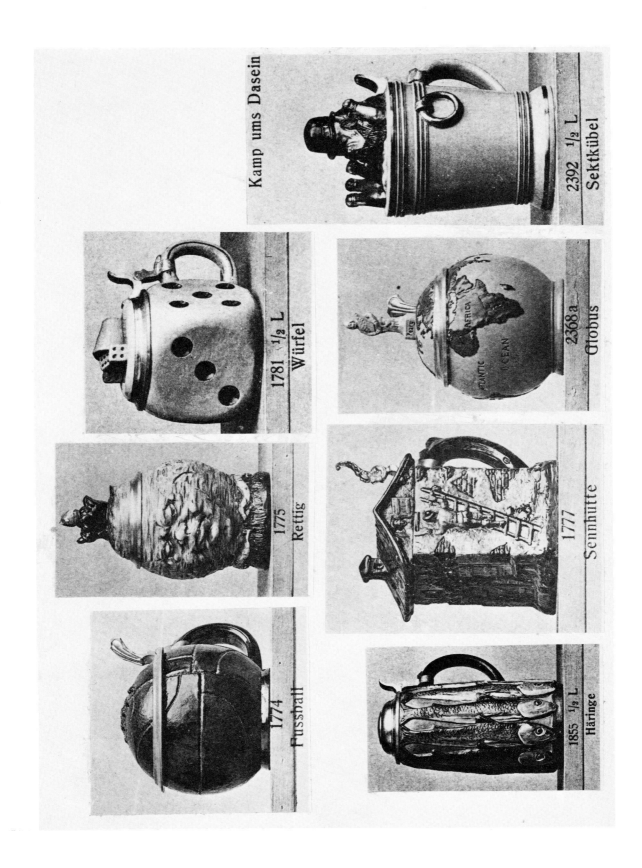

Kamp ums Dasein

2392 ½ L
Sektkübel

1781 ½ L
Würfel

2368a
Globus

1775
Rettig

1777
Sennhütte

1774
Fussball

1855 ½ L
Häringe

INDEX

Color photos appear in italic type.

O.C. = Old Catalogs